What C

Chris   ~~~~~~

"I could not put it down!" – *Jennifer Strutz (Oregon)*

"This book has filled a void in my life as it will fill in the lives of all who read it. Mike Wilson has opened his home, his marriage, and his heart in order to help prepare every Christian to meet the challenge of severe trials. For those of us who have not faced cancer, Mike has offered priceless insights into how we can be an aid and comfort to those battling this disease. For those who will face cancer or who are presently undergoing treatment, Mike's book is a vital encouragement and a ray of hope. Above all, Mike turns our eyes heavenward, to the God of all comfort, who alone has the power to heal. This is a wonderful book, one that you will want to keep nearby to read and reread. But beware, once you begin the first paragraph, you will be hooked. You will not just be starting a book, you will be embarking on a journey. – *Berry Kercheville (Arkansas)*

"Mike's account of his beloved Cheryl's battle with cancer is riveting, touching and sobering all at once. If you have any experience with cancer - and who doesn't? - you will benefit greatly from Mike's insights."
                                        – *David Posey (California)*

"Mike Wilson's new book, *Christians and Cancer: a journey of hope* has heart. It has emotion. I laughed. I cried. It is biblically based and expresses, in layman's terms, interesting and convincing arguments concerning the treatment of this dreaded disease. Most of all, it is a book of hope. I recommend it highly." – *Dee Bowman (Texas)*

"Wow!" – *Carol Conner (North Carolina)*

"This is a book about one family's struggle with cancer, but it is so much more than that. Mike's book is open, honest and profound. He reveals through his and Cheryl's faith-centered experiences with cancer the awesome power of God's provisions for his children: comfort for suffering from his Word and through prayer, support of amazing scope from his Christian family, and the often-neglected aspects of the physical world he created which offers those who are suffering our body's own healing power. Though the book centers on Cheryl's specific struggles and triumphs, it reminds us that all these resources are available to God's children all the time. From personal experience I know how life-threatening disease can show us just how much God loves us and provides for us, the truth which is a foundation of hope not just for this life, but for the one here-after. I found Mike's book a wonderful reminder." – *Jill Buchanan (Mississippi)*

Christians and Cancer

a journey of hope

By

Mike Wilson

Dedication

This book is affectionately dedicated to all of the Lord's people who have bombarded heaven's throne with prayers for my wife. Our own prayer is that God would return the blessing.

Contents

Introduction

*"Trust in the LORD with all your heart, and do
not lean on your own understanding.
    In all your ways acknowledge him, and he will
make straight your paths."* Proverbs 3:5-6

Many books on spirituality and cancer contain assorted
devotional thoughts while failing to give adequate
attention to how the Bible actually functions in the laboratory
of life. The present book addresses this deficiency, underscoring the God-given support system available to Christians who
experience life-threatening disease. However, it is not written
in the style of a step-by-step training manual. Just as the Bible
itself is full of real-life examples that grab our attention, I
have wrapped the applications of this volume around a real
person who is very special to me.

Much of this work is a spiritual journal focused on my
wife, Cheryl, who was diagnosed with a rare and aggressive
type of breast cancer in early 2004. Recording these thoughts
has given me a therapeutic outlet for the flood of emotions
that has accompanied her battle with cancer. As the author, I
have a secret weapon, which I hope will provide the reader

an added bonus. The woman I married is a redheaded fireball, and when the Lord handed out personalities, He gave her a double portion. It is impossible to capture in the pages of a book Cheryl's zest for life, humor, boundless personality and expressive love. The human spirit cannot be reduced to paper and ink, hardbound at the edges, only to be placed on a shelf. Personalities full of life cannot be contained, and Cheryl is certainly full of something. Living with her all these years has been a nonstop adventure. She finds entertainment in the simplest of things, and she has a way with words, as you will see from the pages that follow.

As a preacher of the gospel of Christ, I cannot face adversity of this nature without looking at it from a spiritual angle. Most of my sermon illustrations are experiences from everyday life. I have included at the end of each chapter some Biblical thoughts and excerpts from sermons preached during critical stages of Cheryl's illness, and you will be able to detect some of my own struggles as a supportive husband. The sense of helplessness experienced by *mates* of cancer victims is reflected in these vignettes. I have given 30 years of my life to an in-depth study of God's Word, but the experiences described in the following pages forced me to see certain passages of Scripture from an entirely new perspective.

The title, *Christians and Cancer,* is somewhat misleading in light of the highly personal story that follows. The truth of the matter is that Christians have widely divergent views on how to battle cancer, but there are coping mechanisms accessible to God's people that are unavailable outside of Christ and His church. The year 2004 was a horrible nightmare for our family, in many respects, but it was also a period in which the Lord opened our eyes to the fullness of His blessings. This volume is intended to be a testament to the power of prayer, the generosity of brothers and sisters in Christ, and most of all, the benevolent kindness of our gracious Lord.

Moreover, what our family has experienced may be help-ful to other Christians who are facing similar battles. Sometime within the first year of Cheryl's diagnosis, news reports indicated that cancer surpassed heart disease as the nation's number one killer. Even as my wife suffered through the initial stages of her treatment, dear friends across the country were being diagnosed with various types of cancer. Several have died. When I travel, people in different places have remarked that they have never heard of such a rash of cases occurring everywhere. Cancer is indeed on the rise, and I believe we are seeing only the tip of the iceberg.

For that reason, this book also addresses the decision-making process concerning how Christians *ought to* fight cancer. For example, what are the spiritual dimensions of the cancer experience? Does the Bible offer any help in choosing between conventional versus alternative treatment options? Most Christians have not given sufficient thought to these matters, in the context of competing philosophies that exist in modern society, but they will be raised in the narrative which follows. Whether or not you fully agree with the reasoning presented, one thing is certain: the Lord's people, armed with a Biblical perspective, have a huge advantage over unbelievers when facing life-threatening illness. A Christian's personal faith affects his mental outlook, his mind-body relationship, and his ability to place adversity in its proper perspective. There are, indeed, many benefits to being a child of God during such a crisis.

I suppose I should offer a word of caution up front to readers. Since Cheryl has suffered from cancer of the *breast,* and humor is one of her strong suits, I have captured some of her self-deprecating and hilarious one-liners regard-ing this sensitive portion of the female anatomy. My genuine hope is that readers will be sympathetic toward the dilemma that has been placed on my shoulders. I do not wish to be vulgar or offensive in the slightest, but I trust that you will be able to share our laughter over some of these funny moments. Every effort has been made to convey this humor in good taste, without crossing the line of decency.

Though I have attempted to capture a sometimes gut-wrenching and often heartwarming storyline, this book is intended to be practical and useful. The chapter headings will resonate with other cancer victims, who have undergone similar treatments and challenges. My greatest hope is that if you or a loved one must travel the same road, there will be something in these pages to empower you to exercise strong faith in God, whose promises never fail. To Him be the glory in this life and forevermore!

Chapter 1

Diagnosis: the Initial Shock

"In those days Hezekiah became sick and was at the point of death. And Isaiah the prophet the son of Amoz came to him, and said to him, 'Thus says the LORD: Set your house in order, for you shall die, you shall not recover.'" Isaiah 38:1

On the afternoon of Tuesday, February 24, 2004, Cheryl and I sat alone in the surgeon's office at Medical Center East in Birmingham. We waited anxiously for what seemed like an eternity. The previous Friday morning she had gone to the hospital for a core needle biopsy of her right breast. Was it a harmless cyst, or was it cancer? The pathologist's report was complete, and now it was only a matter of minutes before the news would break.

At least a year and a half earlier, my wife had noticed what appeared to be an ever-so-slight lump on the side of the breast, almost near her ribcage. After a brief period of procrastination, she finally went in for an exam and mammogram. The results showed absolutely nothing and she was cleared. The doctor recommended regular checkups every six months to monitor the situation, but she calmed Cheryl's fears and was not overly concerned about the matter. A half-year later, there was no appreciable change, and both a mammogram and ultrasound came back clear. The tests revealed no measurable tumor or detectable mass characteristic of breast cancer.

Then, suddenly, in late December 2003 and early 2004, the breast became tender and inflamed, with the beginnings of reddish patches of skin. And just as suddenly, in the first days of January, the swelling and tenderness were noticeable and increasing rapidly. Day by day, the deformity was getting worse and it began to really hurt. Cheryl scheduled an immediate appointment with her gynecologist, who took one look and sent her immediately to a surgeon who practiced medicine at the same center. In order to rule out mastitis, or breast infection, he put her on two rounds of powerful antibiotics that lasted for several weeks. At first there seemed to be a reduction in the swelling, but, in the end, the problem persisted and a biopsy had to be done.

As this process unfolded, there was mention of the possibility of inflammatory breast cancer, or IBC. On the evening before we met to hear the results of the biopsy, I did a little Internet research, and what I discovered absolutely terrified me. IBC is a rare and highly aggressive form of breast cancer usually not detected by mammogram or ultrasounds, as it grows in nests or sheets rather than a lump. Comprising perhaps only one to four percent of all cases of breast cancer, it is often misdiagnosed as a breast infection. It is classified as an advanced cancer with poor prognosis. Even though the onset can be very sudden, lymphatic invasion is assumed. Even with advances in treatment, the five-year survival rate is no better than 40%. Until recently, the average lifespan after diagnosis was only a year and a half.

During the biopsy, which occurred on Friday, February 20, there was no fluid to extract from the swollen area. This was not a good sign, because we had hoped that the swelling was due to a cyst, or pocket of fluid that could be drained. Since other options had been ruled out, I had strong suspicions of the worst case scenario. I did not want to be an alarmist, but on Monday night, before our Tuesday office visit, I made a calculated decision to issue a warning to Cheryl. I told her for the first time that if she tested positive for inflammatory breast cancer, we would not be fighting to save her breast. We would be fighting for her life. After a miserable night of little sleep, she really gave it to me the next morning. In retrospect, however, what I told her actually softened the heavier blow that would soon come.

After the young surgeon finally walked into the office that Tuesday afternoon, he sat down and seemed a little nervous when he said, "It *is* cancer.... It's in the higher stages." The initial diagnosis was "infiltrating lobular carcinoma" that presented itself as "inflammatory breast cancer." The rest of what he said is a blur. He informed us that the current standard protocol for this type of cancer is chemotherapy, followed by surgery, followed by radiation. He indicated that we would have to consider our options carefully and determine whether to do treatment at Medical Center East or perhaps transfer to the University of Alabama-Birmingham medical system. Knowing UAB Hospital's reputation as one of the best in the country, we did not hesitate. The doctor made some calls and set up an appointment for an oncology evaluation at the Kirklin Clinic, next to the University Hospital, exactly one week later.

When the doctor left the office to make those phone calls, we felt very much alone. Cheryl broke down and tearfully told me that everything was going to be okay, that after she died I should remarry, but that I needed to take great care to choose a woman who would be a good step-mother to the children. My reaction to those words was, "Now just wait a minute! You don't have a foot in the grave just yet." We reaffirmed our love for each other, and I told her we were going to fight this thing and that with God's help she could win.

We walked out of the doctor's office teary-eyed, stunned, and somewhat apprehensive about the future. Cheryl decided that she needed urgent help from her fellow Christians and from her heavenly Father. She immediately called Richard Buchanan, one of the elders of the Edward's Lake Church of Christ, where I preach. She went over to his home for prayer and consolation. That evening, five spiritual shepherds, accompanied by their wives, gathered in our living room, weeping with us, and holding Cheryl's hand, one by one, while offering the most beautiful prayers to Almighty God. Cheryl was definitely thinking of James 5:14, which says, *"Is anyone among you sick? Let him call for the elders of the church, and let them pray over him, anointing him with oil in the name of the Lord."* I believe there are first-century cultural factors behind the "anointing with oil" statement, but I'm quite certain Cheryl would have pulled out some olive oil without much provocation. In any case, the prayers said that evening were a wonderful comfort to our family.

Edward's Lake spiritual shepherds: Ralph Scott, Richard Buchanan, Chris Ellis, Keith Poe, and Joel Ellis

Later that night, emotionally spent and still in a daze, I sent an email to a few select friends. The last paragraph stated, "Needless to say, this news has turned our family life upside down, as we are struggling to make sense of it all and cope with it. Please pray for us and especially for Cheryl. We have a lot of beloved brothers and sisters in Christ across the country, and we're counting on your help to get us through this." Little did I realize the lightning speed with which that email would be re-circulated. By the following evening, prayers were being said for us at midweek services all over the country. Soon, we found out, Cheryl's name was being lifted up to heaven not only in English, but also in Italian, in German, and in Romanian.

Sermon Excerpt
"All Things Work Together for Good," preached on February 29, 2004

When my good friend and brother in Christ, Ron Masters, was about to die of a cruel brain tumor in his early 40s, I read to him a passage of scripture that has given me tremendous personal comfort and strength – Romans 8:31-39.

What then shall we say to these things? If God is for us, who can be against us? He who did not spare his own Son but gave him up for us all, how will he not also with him graciously give us all things? Who shall bring any charge against God's elect? It is God who justifies. Who is to condemn? Christ Jesus is the one who died – more than that, who was raised – who is at the right hand of God, who indeed is interceding for us. Who shall separate us from the love of

Christ? Shall tribulation, or distress, or persecution, or famine, or nakedness, or danger, or sword? As it is written,

> *"For your sake we are being killed all the day long;*
> *we are regarded as sheep to be slaughtered."*

No, in all these things we are more than conquerors through him who loved us. For I am sure that neither death nor life, nor angels nor rulers, nor things present nor things to come, nor powers, nor height nor depth, nor anything else in all creation, will be able to separate us from the love of God in Christ Jesus our Lord.

In Romans 8:35, Paul asks, "Who shall separate us from the love of Christ?" The answer is *no one.* In Christ, God's love for us and our love for Him meet. We are not promised insulation from suffering in the here and now. What we *are* promised is that no existing force in the universe – terrestrial or celestial – can rob us of the eternal provisions God has made for us. In this life, I may not know what the future holds, but I know *who* holds the future. In the context of eternity, all things work together for good.

Chapter 2

Gearing Up for Battle

"When Jesus saw him lying there and knew that he had already been there a long time, he said to him, 'Do you want to be healed?'" John 5:6

"Commit your work to the LORD, and your plans will be established." Proverbs 16:3

We spent most of Tuesday, March 2 at the Kirklin Clinic adjacent to UAB Hospital in downtown Birmingham, transferring medical records, pathology slides and films, as well as getting on board with a team of cutting-edge physicians there. It is an impressive place, and we believed she would get excellent care. Cheryl had some natural fears but a strong faith, and all in all her spirits were good, even if she was emotionally drained.

We discovered that she would likely start chemotherapy eight days later. It would initially be an outpatient procedure four times, at 21-day intervals. She would also be part of a clinical study to determine how different types of breast cancer cells react to chemotherapy. We were told that after the 84 days of treatment, a determination would be made as to what to do next, whether surgery or more chemo. We would have to gear up for a long and arduous ordeal in an effort to beat this cancer.

Three positives, however slight, resulted from our day there. First, the radiation therapist hinted that there were no signs of cancer on prior mammogram films, and that Cheryl "did everything [she] could" to detect this as early as possible. Second, there were no signs of lumps in the under-arm near the affected breast, which gave us hope that the cancer was localized. Third, the lead doctor, a research scientist at UAB, indicated that although relapse was a very real threat, the initial doses of chemotherapy stood a good chance of eliminating all appearances of the cancer, for the moment at least, and to give Cheryl some fairly quick relief to the swollen area that was causing so much pain. Another positive, as far as we are concerned, is that the physicians had no objection to all the natural supplements she was taking. This included fresh fruit and vegetable juice and several cancer-fighting vitamins. In fact, they wanted a list.

Any cancer victim has a range of conventional and alter-native treatment options from which to choose. In fact, as soon as the word got out, we were literally inundated with advice from scores of people. Some folks suggested we leave the area and get expert care somewhere else. Others insisted that we had to try certain alternative approaches. Finally, there were friends who suggested that the strongest chemotherapy tolerable was the only way to go. Some of the advice was invaluable, some of it was downright extreme, and nearly all of it was passionately expressed. We appreci-ated others' concern, but we had to make some decisions – our *own* decisions – and we felt we did not have a lot of time.

During those first weeks, I combined a lot of praying with some massive research. I have long been somewhat skeptical of mainstream cancer treatments, for reasons I will go into later. However, we were dealing with a challenge that was way over our heads, and we wanted the best expertise we could get. A respected friend, Ed Harrell, suggested the Lord may have providentially put us in Birmingham when we moved there a year and a half earlier, since the medical care at UAB is among the finest in the world. Given the fact that UAB is especially acclaimed for cutting edge breast cancer research, we tended to agree. For the time being, we wanted the best of both worlds, conventional and otherwise. The natural diet and supplements I had researched for Cheryl would complement mainstream approaches, at least initially.

Nevertheless, we were determined not to put our ultimate faith in modern medical science. At the time, many people suggested to us naively that all hope was not lost, because "recent advances in medical care" offered hope. We knew better. Doctors are merely human, and certain diseases seem daunting to them. Inflammatory breast cancer falls in that category. During our initial appointment, when I asked the oncologist assigned to our case if UAB had some success with inflammatory breast cancer, she hesitated, then, after a long moment of silence, gave a rather evasive, affirmative answer: "Yes... *some* success." A bad politician could have offered more hope. It was a telltale sign, and a foretaste of something she would later say that was unequivocally negative.

Cheryl underwent a CT scan on Friday, March 5 for evidence of breast cancer metastasis in her lungs and liver, and a nuclear scan on Monday, March 8 to see if the bones were affected. The preliminary results were: clear, clear and clear. In fact, when the phone call came for results of the CT scan, Cheryl was a ball of nerves and too rattled to take the call, so she handed the phone to me and waited anxiously while I talked with the nurse. There was no evidence of tumors in Cheryl's chest, which was good news, because breast cancer often reappears in the lungs first. She did have a small spot on the liver, but the technician reported it was probably a cyst or something like a fatty deposit not related to her cancer. Everything else looked completely normal. Needless to say, Cheryl and I were overjoyed by the report! We immediately offered a prayer of thanksgiving together.

We braced ourselves for a long battle. We spent hours juicing fruits and vegetables, especially carrots, and flooded Cheryl's immune system with healthy nutrients. I spent entire days in waiting rooms while Cheryl went through test after test. And because she was in the clinical study, the doctors wanted even more data before the start of chemo. Consequently, they pushed back the target date for the first infusion to the following Monday, March 15. The long wait was agonizing.

I started sending regular email updates to spread the news to friends and fellow Christians. One of the early dispatches says, "We have literally been inundated with cards, flowers, phone calls, emails, and expressions of kindness from all over the world, and we can barely read everything, let alone assimilate it or respond to everyone. It is humbling to have so many people praying for you, and our prayer is that God would 'return the favor' by extending His richest blessings on all those who have been kind enough to pray for us at this difficult time. You have our deepest gratitude. If the Lord graciously decides to extend Cheryl's life, we will acknowledge that the power does not reside in human formulas, either conventional or natural. 'Prayer therapy' is the best treatment of all, and all the glory will go to God Almighty, who is on the throne this very moment. To Him be the glory!"

Brooke, Megan, Cheryl and Mike, right after the diagnosis, in March 2004. Courtesy of Gilbert Photography.

**Sermon Excerpt
"Confronted with Suffering,"
preached on March 14, 2004**

Adversity forces us to focus on principles of scripture that will help us achieve spiritual victory and become more useful servants. We may see the reasons for it more clearly only in retrospect. There are five God-given coping mechanisms that have aided us in Cheryl's struggle in recent weeks.

1. Hope in God. Bad things happen to people. Suffering is a part of life, and no one is exempt. The bottom line is that when facing it you have only two choices: lose all hope and give up, or hang on to the only real hope we have in times of crisis (Rom. 5:1-5). When the pressure is on, hope is staying power, to hold up rather than fold up.

25

2. Take it one day at a time. It's so easy to get caught up in long-term prognosis, and what the future holds. Each of us has the seeds of a terminal disease right now (Gen. 3). When you live in the future, you fail to appreciate the present. You miss the joy of living at the moment. Every day is a gift. When you have the "abundant life" now, and heaven waiting for you, why worry about tomorrow?

3. Be thankful. When bad news hits, it's easy to become bitter and say, "Why me? Why this? Why now? Life isn't fair!" Suffering is an opportunity to appreciate what you once took for granted. Philip Yancey tells the story of a restaurant visit at Yellowstone National Park. When *Old Faithful* erupted, tourists were mesmerized, but not a single waiter or busboy even bothered to look up. *Old Faithful* had become so familiar that it lost its ability to impress them. Lamentations 3:22-24 says, *"The steadfast love of the LORD never ceases; his mercies never come to an end; they are new every morning; great is your faithfulness. 'The LORD is my portion,' says my soul, 'therefore I will hope in him.'"* With God's blessings, every day is a new day. You may discover new blessings and new opportunities never before realized (Phil. 4:4-7).

4. Get refocused on what's really important. It's amazing how what seemed so important on February 23 could be so mundane and inconsequential on February 24. Life is nothing but a passing "vapor," full of uncertainty (James 4:14-17). Suffering is an opportunity to get your priorities in order.

5. Make sure you're right with God. This life is a probationary period, and you've got one chance (2 Cor. 5:6-10). This is it! If you miss heaven, you miss out on everything that is anything. C. S. Lewis said, "Pain is God's megaphone to rouse a deaf world."

One day, sooner or later, you will likely have an opportunity to suffer intensely. You can either wallow in self-pity or you can rise up in faith. It will be an opportunity to really *live your faith.*

Chapter 3

Chemotherapy, a.k.a. "Killer-mo"

"And there was a woman who had had a discharge of blood for twelve years, and who had suffered much under many physicians, and had spent all that she had, and was no better but rather grew worse. She had heard the reports about Jesus and came up behind him in the crowd and touched his garment."
Mark 5:25-27

Cheryl's first chemotherapy treatment occurred Monday, March 15. She was in some pain going into it because there was an extensive biopsy, taken earlier the same day, as part of the clinical study. University Hospital is very much a research facility, affiliated with UAB Medical School, and there were times when Cheryl felt like a laboratory rat, even though everyone was gracious during the testing process.

In March Madness that year, UAB's basketball team upset Kentucky to make it to the Sweet 16, which was fitting, since Cheryl loves college basketball. In some ways, we had our own March Madness with "infusion therapy." The chemotherapeutic agents used for the first four rounds, at 21-day intervals, were Taxol and Carboplatin. During the first two days after the initial treatment, Cheryl felt like her normal self. Days three, four, and five were rough, with a lot of joint pain and general achy feeling all over.

We took a planned, short trip the weekend of March 20-23 to Panama City, Florida, and she did fine. Then she brought back with her a bad cold, which she shared with me. The doctor checked her white blood cell count, which was on the low side of "normal," and gave her some antibiotics as a precautionary measure. Over the next five months, we continued to do a lot of juicing and vitamin therapy. All in all, Cheryl's spirits were good and she was determined to win this battle. In the preliminary rounds of chemo, she exceeded my expectations with her cheerfulness and energy level, though there were many days in which "the spirit was willing, but the flesh was weak."

Perhaps the whole ordeal took its toll on my own stress level. As all of this was unfolding, I awoke a few times with some chest pains and decided to have it checked out. Results showed a "borderline EKG" with a potential problem on the left side of my heart. My doctor ordered a treadmill stress test, and it also revealed at least a slight abnormality. The medical group ordered an immediate nuclear stress test to study possible blockages in my coronary blood vessels. Could both of us be experiencing life-threatening illnesses at the same time? The nuclear test results usually take five business days or so. However, the Edward's Lake congregation just happens to have a prominent cardiologist, Randy Harrison, affiliated with the cardiovascular center where I had the testing done. Randy was on a hunting trip but called in so he could deliver same-day, VIP information to me. The test results were "normal," which means I either had some false positives on the preliminary tests or some slight irregularities. I did breathe a huge sigh of relief, and it allowed me to continue being a caregiver for Cheryl's needs instead of a heart patient on the receiving end of care.

It did not take long for the inevitable to happen. By Saturday, April 3, Cheryl was losing so much hair that she commissioned me to shave off the rest. I was a bit nervous doing it. As for Cheryl, it was rather traumatic because her red hair is one of the things she really likes about herself. I assured her it would grow back, and we threw the locks on the ground in the back yard, at her request, "so the birds could use it to build their nests." It is not Cheryl's style to wear a wig, even though she had been fitted for one. She wore a simple hat to church the following day, and our daughters Megan and Brooke also wore hats to show support for Mom. What we didn't expect is that when we walked into the building that morning, 35 or 40 sisters in Christ also donned hats to demonstrate their solidarity as well. Never did a bunch of ladies in hats look so beautiful! It was truly special, and tears welled up in Cheryl's eyes.

The "hat" sisters reenacting the event about a year later

As the weeks and treatments progressed, she experienced more of a lingering joint pain, particularly in her left hip and leg, as well as numbness in her toes – all symptoms that are not entirely unexpected. There were days of severe nausea, and the steroids prescribed in conjunction with chemotherapy caused her to bounce off the walls. Her own nickname for chemo was "killer-mo." The chemo-induced arthritic symptoms rendered her virtually immobile at times, and the pain in her joints was intense. Family members, friends, and sisters in Christ spent many hours rubbing and applying soothing lotions to her feet.

There were other effects as well. At the beginning of treatment, we were informed that chemotherapy would throw Cheryl into menopause, and it did. She was 45 years old at the time, so she may have been on the verge of crossing this milestone anyway. The frequent hot flashes were in many respects mild compared to the other physical challenges she faced, but they certainly added to her misery. Perhaps the most unexpected symptom was mental in nature. After treatment started, Cheryl was certain that her mind did not process information as fast or as clearly as she was accustomed, and she became extremely forgetful and somewhat disoriented at times. The oncologist confirmed that sometimes chemotherapy presented some special mental challenges consistent with Cheryl's description of the problem. Cheryl would later make occasional excuses for herself, on the grounds of "chemo brain."

Throughout this period, there were times when I seriously wondered whether we were doing the wisest thing by undergoing conventional therapy at all. I had serious concerns about the effectiveness of chemo, and whether it would cripple Cheryl's immune system, precisely at a time when we needed to boost it the most. Although I had great respect for the medical expertise of the UAB physicians, generally speaking, I playfully spoke of the oncologist, surgeon, and radiologist as

Cheryl's *poison* doctor, *cut* doctor, and *burn* doctor.

As Cheryl settled into a chemotherapy routine, she accumulated a stylish collection of hats and other headgear for outings in public, especially for church assemblies. One time, a baby in the pew behind us tried to pull off Cheryl's hat. Fortunately, the mother came to the rescue before the deed was done, because Cheryl hates to present herself in any way that smacks of immodesty, and this would have definitely opened her up to playful accusations of indecent exposure. I tried to reassure her that she was still the most beautiful girl in the world to me, but in a lighter moment I told her we could make a science fiction film, and she could play the alien. In fact, when a family generously brought dinner one night, Cheryl forgot that she was uncovered. When the good sister remarked what a cute bare head she had, Cheryl fled from her nakedness and grabbed a hat! For some reason, we had never seen her run so fast, in spite of the joint pain.

A child's view of Cheryl's "chemo" appearance. Can you guess which one is Cheryl? Courtesy of Sarah Embry.

Over the next few months, we had several waves of company from out of town. We have a lot of close friends across the country, and when we lived in California, so many of them visited that we dubbed our home the "Wilson Hotel." Now many of the same friends and family wanted to come and "help out." We were grateful for the help, but, with Cheryl sometimes flat on her back, we warned them all not to expect the type of gracious hospitality that we normally try to deliver. On one such occasion, when we combined church company with out-of-town company, I killed a snake meandering in the front yard. It gave to our household a whole new meaning to the phrase, "snake in the grass." Unfortunately, my hoe was dull and I had to whack the thing about ten times before finishing the job. I used the incident to warn potential out-of-town company that they might want to reconsider, largely to no avail.

By the end of May, Cheryl had her fourth chemo infusion. The doctor wanted to delay, as her white blood count was low, but our oldest daughter Megan was graduating from high school, and we had vacation reservations the following week. Since the medical team did not want to wait till we returned from the trip, the doctor ordered a lesser dosage of chemo, along with a shot to build up her white cell count.

The roughest part of that day occurred when the doctor, a foreign-born oncologist and research specialist, made her rounds during the infusion and pretty much dropped a bomb on Cheryl's prognosis. The doctor basically said that she expected Cheryl to die of breast cancer. She added that it was not the remaining cancer in the breast that concerned her, but the inevitable cells floating around which can invade the lungs, liver or bones. She said that the original mass was too large for this not to be a likely scenario, and the chances of beating it were somewhat formidable. I took the oncologist aside, and upon further questioning, she finally admitted that survival is possible, and that they would do everything to increase Cheryl's chances. However, there was no real hope in her words or body language, and she thought it was her duty to prepare us for the worst-case scenario. Since Cheryl felt pretty well at the time, the tumor was shrinking, and she had such a strong determination to survive, it was not what she wanted to hear. In fact, she was beside herself. Perhaps as much as anything, what bothered us was the poor bedside manner in which the message was delivered.

With a long day at the cancer center and a compromised immune system, Cheryl insisted on going to midweek Bible class that night and asking the elders of the Edward's Lake church to pray for her once again, just as they had done when the diagnosis first hit. They took turns holding her hand and bringing wonderfully worded sentiments before the throne of heaven on her behalf, invoking God's mercy, care, and healing power. That night we remembered that God granted King Hezekiah an additional 15 years of life, and that He could certainly do it for Cheryl, if He chose to do so.

A few days later, we departed on a family "graduation trip" to Washington, D.C., and down the Atlantic coast to Williamsburg, Virginia and New Bern, North Carolina. In the process we met up with some good friends in those states. Going into it, Cheryl's white blood count was low and we had our worries about her, but she showed unusual resiliency and weathered it all magnificently. During some days she napped a little while the rest of us did the tourist thing, but most of the time she was eager to go see the sights and eat the good food. Unfortunately or fortunately, depending on one's perspective, she had to depart somewhat from her strict dietary regimen and ingest a few delicacies.

After we returned home, Cheryl's next medical visit showed a reduced cancerous mass in her mammogram and ultrasound, and a surgical consultation urged continued chemotherapy to shrink it more, as much as possible, before surgery and radiation. The surgeon is respected across the country and was generally positive in his assessments. Anything positive resonated with us at that point. After a good deal of reflection, we decided to fire the oncologist with the poor manners, as Cheryl insisted on someone with a more optimistic demeanor and outlook.

On Wednesday, June 9, we met with the new oncologist, who had an absolutely wonderful way of connecting with us. It's amazing what a difference a doctor's optimism can make. Without trying to give us false hope, this doctor was upbeat in her assessments, extremely well-informed about cutting-edge treatment options, and actually willing to talk about exploring them. From that time forward, she also sat down with us, took a lot of time during each visit and patiently answered our questions. Cheryl's previous oncologist had possessed none of these qualities.

The new doctor immediately put Cheryl on a more aggressive regimen of chemotherapy, a combination of Cytoxan and Adriamycin every two weeks. The goal was to shrink the cancer in the right breast down to "almost nothing." This would optimize the benefit from surgery and reduce chances for recurrence at the site – an absolute must when dealing with inflammatory breast cancer. The oncologist informed us that doing this treatment every two weeks seems to increase chances of survival, according to clinical studies, but it would require a couple of extra "adjuvant" shots – one to boost white blood cell production and another to stimulate the manufacture of red blood cells. Without this extra bone marrow stimulus, the rougher treatment only two weeks apart would have caused her blood counts to drop too much.

This regimen change caused greater trauma, more nausea, and worse soreness in her joints – a general achy feeling all over, like a bad case of the flu. This, in turn, forced Cheryl to do a lot more resting. In fact, she was either in bed or on the couch a whole week after the first treatment. She was really sick. With all her normal get-up-and-go, this put her in the uncomfortable position of being on the receiving end as others served her. A true servant herself, her motto is, "It is more blessed to give than to receive" (Acts 20:35). She could not stand the thought of not being able to get up and vacuum the carpet or prepare a meal. She felt lazy and useless, although we tried to convince her otherwise.

Additionally, her taste buds were completely whacked out. Nothing tasted right. She also had some other symptoms that were partially alleviated by a nice, warm bath. A local sister in Christ gave her some "miracle soap," which seemed to help, in spite of the suspicious designation. The baths were soothing, and Cheryl enjoyed these "rub-a-dub" moments just like a bald-headed baby likes to splash around. If I can be more frank, at one point I asked her, "Is there anything I can get for you?" Her reply was, "A new bottom."

During the second infusion therapy of this new chemo regimen, Cheryl asked me to pray for a young man with liver cancer in the next bedside. It was late afternoon, and as I finished the prayer, I noticed that virtually every eye, from patients to nurses, was focused in my direction. At first, I felt a bit awkward about being the center of attention. Then a breast cancer patient across the room called out, "What about me? I want some!" I went over, introduced myself, and said a prayer for her as well. I am not a *hospital chaplain*, but it occurred to me that day how people tend to be more open to spiritual things in a chemotherapy center.

By the end of June, the oncologist informed us, "The baseline of the cancerous mass is almost nonexistent." In fact, she added that if she hadn't been treating Cheryl, she would not be able to recognize the cancerous breast at all. The treatment was working, making surgery by mid-August a virtual certainty. Cheryl's right breast had almost returned to normal, and the original pain was completely gone. The downside of that visit is that the oncologist, for all her positive outlook, confirmed my suspicions regarding any future metastasis. If the cancer were to spread to other organs, she said, there is little that modern science could do to influence a complete healing. If Cheryl was to survive, we would have to draw our line in the sand on there being no recurrence.

In the latter part of those vicious five months of chemotherapy, Cheryl found a great hobby to pass the hours away, while doing something productive and keeping her mind active. She took old family photos and arranged them into creative albums for both of the girls. It reminded her of precious family memories and put a smile on her face. She set up a table in the bedroom and had her own "craft shop." It was something she could do when she felt well, without being overburdened, and it helped her to keep her mind off the pain when she did not feel her best.

On July 25, we watched the television as Lance Armstrong won the sixth of seven straight *Tour de France* championships. Although I did not agree with elements of his personal life, the fact that he beat cancer after it had spread to his lungs and brain, and then went on to win the most grueling event in sports so many times before retiring, was an inspiration to us. To me, Cheryl was an even better role model. She continued running the race of faith without wavering. Her godly character and optimism were transparent, even when she wasn't feeling well. She would typically say, "At least I feel better than yesterday!" or "It's not as bad as it could be." She was somewhat fearful of dying, but she refused to let this defeat her.

Letter to Mom

About five years prior to Cheryl's diagnosis, my mother died of cancer one day before her 58th birthday. Like my wife, she also had red hair. Together, they have been the two most influential people in my life. Unfortunately, the proximity with which they both had to battle life-threatening cancer invited some unpleasant comparisons in my mind. I wrote this letter to my mother just a couple of weeks before she passed away.

May 6, 1999
Dear Mom,

I hope this letter finds you in good spirits, in spite of all the pain and bad news that have devastated your life in recent weeks. I'm proud to have a mom who has endured such a trial with courage and grace. You are an example to us all.

So many people build their lives on false hopes. Modern science never displays its impotence more profoundly than when a doctor says, "There's nothing more that we can do." What do they know, anyway? I'm so happy we have a Great Physician who gives us hope, even when no one else can.

I want to thank you for all the love and countless hours of watchful care that you have invested in my life. A little guy could not have had a better mother!

My love affair with the Bible began with your example. Do you remember that time when I was a teenager and I asked you why you were reading the Bible in bed? You gave me a short synopsis of Job and all the problems he faced. From then on, I decided to read the Bible on my own, too, and I haven't stopped since!

39

I cannot imagine a life on earth without you, but I know the day is coming. When the passage of death arrives, we are not hurled into isolation. One begins to "see the invisible." I appreciate the description of Dallas Willard along these lines:

"Poor Lazarus dies, we are told by Jesus, 'and he was borne away by the angels to where God's people are gathered' (Luke 16:22). From the 'great cloud of witnesses' come those who have been watching for us. They greet us and enfold us. And while those first few moments or hours will surely present us with one astonishing view after another, we will be joyous and peaceful because of the company we are in.

"...The old spiritual song says, 'I looked over Jordon and what did I see, comin' for to carry me home? A band of angels comin' after me, comin' for to carry me home.' And this seemingly simplistic picture, derived from scriptural stories and teachings, presents exactly what we should expect."[1]

If you get there before I do, please wait for me. And in the time that you have left, please keep us in your prayers as we keep you in ours. The girls send their love.

Your son, always,
Mike

---

[1] Dallas Willard, *The Divine Conspiracy* (San Francisco: Harper, 1998), p. 397

Chapter 4

Mastectomy: "Unequally Yoked"

"The Lord is my helper; I will not fear; what can man do to me?" Hebrews 13:6

We met with the surgeon on July 20, asked a lot of questions, and scheduled a modified radical mastectomy of the right breast. It would happen on Monday, August 16. I remember thinking how anxious we would be to get results from the post-surgery pathology report. How extensive was the cancer? How many lymph nodes were affected? How successful was the chemotherapy in shrinking the cancer? Would preliminary answers to these questions be able to help us with a general prognosis? The surgeon indicated that the outlook would not significantly change unless the pathology report showed a total disappearance of cancer.

The doctor further explained that inflammatory cancer is like a tree. Chemo might remove the leaves, giving the appearance of massive shrinkage, while the branches are still there. He informed us that whether he took one-fourth of the breast or all of it, it would only affect possible recurrence at the site of origin, and not cancer cells attacking other sites in the body. Once again, even though we already knew this, it put Cheryl on an emotional roller coaster. I reminded her how Jay Hunt, a beloved brother in Christ, had ordered her: "No negative thoughts!"

The thought of losing a breast is a traumatic thing for a female, especially in this sex-crazed society. With the type of breast cancer she was fighting, there could be no thought of reconstructive surgery for at least a couple of years. Unlike many cases in which reconstruction almost immediately follows removal of the cancerous breast, it was not even an option for us. Even though Cheryl's physical appearance would be altered dramatically, we didn't question having the mastectomy done, if it could possibly save her life.

A week later, when Cheryl received one of many baskets of carefully wrapped goodies by special delivery, she asked, with tears running down her eyes, "Why do they keep doing this for me?" It was a gift from Rusty and Cindy Holley, a precious couple in our church family, and it was probably the third one they had sent. Each basket from them was custom designed, beautifully ornamented, and no doubt very expensive. I told Cheryl that she was special and that people loved her. She could not quite accept it.

About the same time, we got a card in the mail from Pete and Cathy Kinser, some friends in California. On a visit to Kennedy Space Center, Cathy kept noticing two statements which she shared with us: "Nothing is impossible," and "Failure is not an option." She added, "I thought how these statements would apply to your fight with cancer. When you add God to the mix, what wonderful things can happen!"

The same night, we received word that Mildred Jernigan had suffered a stroke and was in critical situation. Mildred was an elderly saint in southern California who was a constant encouragement to us in our years there in the 1980s and 90s. And then, when Cheryl got sick and Mildred was not doing well herself, she shared with us her prayer to God that she might be taken and Cheryl spared. I'm not always sure what to make of providential circumstances, but I certainly believe that "the prayer of a righteous person has great power" (James 5:16). When we heard the news, I prayed for Mildred, but we could not help but remember her own prayer request. She died the next day.

On Saturday, July 31, we were sitting around a table eating and playing cards, when Cheryl spoke of her doomed breast. Bobbi Barton, a good friend and sister in Christ, suggested she would take the day off to be at the hospital for the mastectomy. Cheryl protested, "There's no reason for you to do that. There's nothing you can do to save *it!*" We all burst out into laughter.

The weeks passed and as the time drew near, Cheryl began to grow a little nervous. On Sunday evening, August 15, we were gathered with the Lord's people for worship. With Cheryl's surgery scheduled for the next morning, Richard Buchanan led the closing song from the center aisle in the middle of the building, directing everyone's attention to "the sister in the blue hat." Everyone turned toward Cheryl, and many wept as we sang, "God will take care of you." Cheryl had to continually wipe the tears away. She hates to be singled out publicly as the center of attention, but she said afterward, "Everybody was looking at me, and I decided to look at each person in the eyes. I could have been a passive participant, but I decided to be an active one."

The next morning, we arrived at the hospital while it was still dark, but several people from church were there waiting for us, and many more came by throughout the day. Heather McMasters, a good friend from California, had flown out to help Cheryl and the girls. The surgery itself lasted for several hours and went well. The pathologist detected no cancer in the skin margin tests during the operation, and the team of doctors was not able to see any evidence of cancer in surrounding tissues. The chemotherapy had shrunk the site sufficiently for surgeons to extract what appeared to be all of the cancer at the site of origin. Cheryl said that when she was rolled into surgery, she imagined the faces of beloved brothers and sisters in Christ standing around her as a great "cloud of witnesses" providing strength and support.

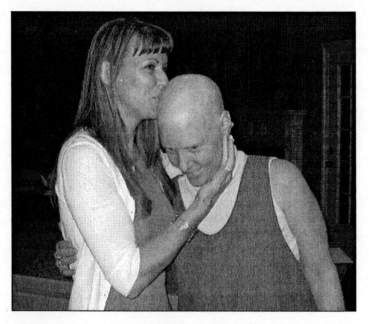

Heather McMasters and Cheryl after chemo and right before surgery, August 2004

Coming out of surgery, the effects of the anesthesia can cause a person to say some funny things. The view of a friend, Joe Smith, is that we all have a filter to guard what we say, but the anesthesia takes out the filter, so the patient's tongue cuts loose with all kinds of interesting and unguarded sentiments. Cheryl told our daughter Megan, "I love you," about ten times in five minutes, as she drifted in and out of consciousness. When I led a prayer of thanksgiving, she confessed, "I think I fell asleep during the prayer." Later that evening, when the surgeon informed her that she wouldn't be able to wear a bra for quite awhile, she protested that she was a preacher's wife, and that she couldn't do such a thing. Perhaps the anesthesia hadn't completely worn off, because when resignation to the idea finally set in, she blurted out, in a veiled allusion to the "hat" incident, "Hurry, get the phone directory, call the ladies, and tell them 'no bras.'" After she came back to full consciousness, she had no memory of ever saying such a thing!

Before the surgery, Cheryl joked about coming out of it "lopsided" and "unequally yoked," adding she'd have to push her left breast to the center to do double duty. After recovery, she was in and out of consciousness but bemoaned that she had been "maimed." Ever trying to be the supportive husband, I repeatedly assured her that her remaining breast was "my favorite one." After a few days at home, humor helped her to cope with the loss of a breast. She talked about being "flat and fluffy," depending on which side one was considering.

She was in her hospital room less than 24 hours, discharged on Tuesday afternoon. In the following days, she showed characteristic spunk and resilience. She laughed, her appetite did not diminish, and she healed nicely, even with tubes draining fluid from the wound area. She even tried to do a little work around the house, though we reminded her more than once to get some rest. Cheryl drew strength from close friends and family. There were many phone calls from loved ones. A visit from Jennifer Strutz of Oregon in the days afterwards helped immensely, and Bobbi Barton was a constant encouragement locally. All the support helped to keep my wife's spirits up.

On Monday August 23, the surgeon called with results of the post-surgery pathology report, and it was not entirely what we were hoping for. The tumor had grown in two different kinds of patterns, one ductal and the other lobular. At the largest spot, it was five centimeters, or about two-and-a-half inches, across. The margins were clear, except they came close to the deepest portion of the breast. There were small nests of cancer in most of the breast tissue. It was estrogen receptor positive – something we already knew – which meant that Cheryl would be treated with Tamoxifen or a similar drug. Then came the biggest blow of all: of 24 lymph nodes removed, 12 still had cancer in them, even after five months of chemo. The surgeon added that there was a "significant chance" that it could reappear in the future elsewhere in her body, and he arranged for an additional consultation with the oncologist before we began radiation. He said the medical team would like to have seen more regression of the tumor, and classified it as "partial regression," even though it seemed significantly reduced after eight rounds of powerful chemotherapy. We did not want to speculate how extensive the cancerous invasion was prior to chemo.

We were desperate for some good news and found consolation in the doctor's belief that they got all of the cancer in the breast itself. The bad news was that Cheryl would still have to fight for her life, with perhaps an even more daunting challenge. At that point, prior to talking with the oncologist, our inclination was *not* to do additional chemotherapy. We wanted to give her own God-given immune system a chance, with all the holistic and natural approaches she was undergoing. By this point, she was now a vegan, abstaining from all animal products as well as sugar. Most of all, we were relying on prayer to Almighty God. We could not beat this on our own, and it was in His hands.

Sermon Excerpt
"God's Unrevealed Commands,"
first preached on May 2, 2004

We generally think of God's commandments as those laws and prohibitions which regulate our behavior on earth. God's commands, however, are not limited to us. After all, He spoke creation into existence (Genesis 1; Psalm 104). And with regard to His providence, Psalm 103:20-21 says, "Bless the LORD, O you his angels, you mighty ones who do his word, obeying the voice of his word. Bless the LORD, all his hosts, his ministers, who do his will!" When God blesses His people, He is said to "command the blessing" on them (Deut. 28:8). When Daniel prayed for an end to Babylonian captivity, he was told, "At the beginning of your pleas for mercy a word went out...." (Daniel 9:23). This, of course, is the same Daniel who said on another occasion, "My God sent his angel and shut the lions' mouths...." (Dan. 6:22).

Just because His activities are not revealed to us does not mean God is inactive. He directs world affairs, intervenes, blesses, interacts, and answers prayers. We will never know much of it in this life, although at times we may have a strong hunch. When God came to Israel's rescue, it was as if he came upon an abandoned girl wallowing in her blood. He saw her and cried out, "Live!" (Ezekiel 16:6). Can He not repeat the same command for someone in desperate need today? "Live!"

One day, the King of the universe will look you in the eye and issue one more command. It will be either, "Enter in," or "Depart from me." The command has not yet been issued, and your life on earth will determine which way it goes. Do you have a genuine faith commitment which, according to the Lord's "great mercy," will enable Him to grant you an "imperishable" inheritance in heaven (1 Pet. 1:3-4)?

Chapter 5

Radiation: "Burnt to a Crisp"

"For the sake of Christ, then, I am content with weaknesses, insults, hardships, persecutions, and calamities. For when I am weak, then I am strong."
2 Corinthians 12:10

In late August, Elaine Laurence sent Cheryl a gift bag full of colored balloons, with a note attached: "Welcome to the world of Inflate-a-Boobs!" (For the full text, see Appendix 3). Elaine is a sister in Christ in the Edward's Lake church, and she happens to be an inflammatory breast cancer survivor for 13 years. What's even more amazing is that she overcame IBC at a time when it was almost a certain death sentence. Consequently, she served as a positive role model to Cheryl and as a reminder that this nemesis could be beaten. Given the prognosis for this disease, even with advanced treatment protocols, it would seem almost miraculous to have two IBC survivors in the same congregation. Could it be possible?

By August 31, the surgeon had basically released Cheryl, and she later quipped, "I'm glad my surgeon cut me off. Well, he cut me off *literally!"* As we left the surgeon's office that day, a nice lady spotted Cheryl's bald head under her hat, and perhaps her half-flat chest, and proudly informed us she had just undergone the finishing touches of breast reconstruction surgery. She told us she got the best reconstructive cosmetic surgeon at UAB, whose name happened to be Dr. Fix. We laughed, but she insisted that was really his name. Reconstruction was not even on our radar screen at the moment.

The previous day, we had consulted with an alternative doctor for the first time, but that story will occupy a separate chapter. As far as conventional treatment was concerned, it was on to the radiologist. In fact, we did not see the oncologist again until late October. When we did, she said there would be no more chemotherapy for the time being. They had already given Cheryl the best stuff they had, and "more is not better," especially with no proof of metastasis yet.

To help ward off recurrence of the cancer, the oncologist put Cheryl on Tamoxifen for about a year. This drug shuts down estrogen receptors on breast cells, stopping them from sending out the "grow and multiply" message. One possible side effect is an increased risk of endometrial cancer in the uterus. On the other hand, the benefit is that it can cut the recurrence rate roughly in half. We believed the benefits outweighed the risks. Generally, Tamoxifen is prescribed for no longer than five years. In Cheryl's case, when the onset of menopause would be clearly established, after about a year, the plan was to switch from Tamoxifen to an aromatase inhibitor. This type of drug blocks estrogen's ability to reach cancer cells and make them grow. Aromatase inhibitors purportedly get slightly better results than Tamoxifen, with fewer side effects.

We met with the radiologist on August 31, the same day of Cheryl's release by the surgeon. She was a younger woman, with a professional demeanor and compassionate disposition. She said, "You've been through it, haven't you?" From the things she proceeded to say, it was obvious that she had done her homework on this new patient. She had taken the time to thoroughly familiarize herself with Cheryl's case history and even brought into the exam room a notepad full of handwritten observations from her reading of the file. She was also determined to increase survival chances with an aggressive treatment plan. There would be two radiation treatments per day for nearly five weeks.

I decided that, in spite of the long drive and the some-times longer waiting periods, I would accompany Cheryl as much as I could, and bring my office work with me to the waiting room. Taking care of Cheryl had essentially become a second fulltime job. She was still recovering from chemotherapy and surgery, and now she was going to be zapped with radiation twice daily. There was constant trans-port to various medical facilities, and, for awhile at least, she really needed someone to drive her back and forth. Additionally, her complementary and alternative therapy had just gone up a few notches. There was the purchase of a wide array of specialty foods and vitamins, food prepara-tion, hours of juicing, and figuring out what was essentially a round-the-clock schedule of constant intake of fresh raw foods and juices. Taking endless phone calls from loved ones, coordinating various kinds of help offered by gener-ous local Christians, and managing the household in areas that Cheryl would normally handle ate up a lot of time. Finally, Cheryl was facing her own emotional battles, and she needed strong support. The elders of the Edward's Lake church were very generous with giving me a flexible work schedule during this time, but something still had to give. I was stretched beyond the limit. Pressure from the whole situation had forced me to devote my full energies to a deli-cate balancing act between doing the Lord's work and trying to help keep my wife alive. I had been one of the

editors of *Focus Magazine,* a monthly publication for growing Christians, for seven years. It was truly a passion of
mine, but I simply had no time for it any longer. Cheryl
asked me to resign, and I complied.

We could not start radiation as soon as the radiologist
desired. In the weeks after surgery, Cheryl had two drains
coming out of her chest, and one of them would not cooper-
ate. We hoped to get it down to 30 ml of fluid per day, but it
persisted for several weeks at 50 ml. Consequently, to
prevent an infection, she was pretty much cooped up at the
house. With her open wound and the drain, we were
cautious about letting her be around very many people.
Because Cheryl is a social person, this nearly drove her
crazy. To compensate for the loneliness and isolation, she
often talked on the phone for about half the day. She wept
on Sunday, September 5 when she sneaked into a Sunday
evening church service for the first time since her surgery.
She was so happy to be around God's people, even if from a
relative distance.

Occasionally during this period she would get out of
the house for a short walk in order to "scare the neighbors –
hatless and *boob-less.*" Actually, she did wear a hat, except
for the one occasion when the wind blew it off! The walks
became a pleasant part of her daily regimen. One enjoyable
part of such excursions involved noticing various nuances
of neighbors' homes and yards. Cheryl loved to study the
landscapes, trees, and plant adornments. We had lived in
Alabama only a couple of years, but we felt it was one of
the best-kept secrets in the country. Trussville, northeast of
Birmingham, is an absolutely delightful town and a great
place to raise kids.

At the time, something else began popping up in the
yards as well. The political season was heating up, and it
was a presidential election year. In conservative Alabama,
one relatively new family in our neighborhood put up a

"Kerry-Edwards" sign in the front yard. The rest of the neighbors were up in arms about it and soon retaliated with "Bush-Cheney" signs in front of almost every house. Driving down the street was an experience: *Bush... Bush... Bush... Bush...* Kerry... *Bush... Bush... Bush...* etc. Only in Alabama! Regardless of one's political leanings, it is generally interesting to snoop a little on the neighbors, and it takes the mind away from *cancerous* thoughts.

Birthdays are usually special occasions in our home, but we were all a little frazzled that year. Consequently, nothing went right on Cheryl's first birthday with cancer, which was Sunday, September 19. Our oldest daughter, Megan, by now a student at Florida College, called at a time when Cheryl was not available to talk. Our younger daughter, Brooke, and I did not prepare a birthday cake or make restaurant plans, given Cheryl's dietary restrictions. I had taken her to an "organic restaurant" the day before, which I hoped would be special, but the food was less than desirable. To make matters worse, I had ordered some unique presents over the Internet, and they arrived late, not in time for her birthday. Finally, my mind was not working properly after preaching a sermon and I gave Brooke permission to go out to lunch with someone other than her mother that Sunday afternoon, and that was the last straw. Perhaps "chemo brain" was contagious! In any case, Cheryl went on a rampage about not being appreciated. The tirade did not fully stop until the next morning, when she admitted to having been possessed with "Saul's evil spirit."

Two days later, September 21, Cheryl finally got her second tube pulled out of her chest, paving the way for the start of radiation. The radiologist and her team drew thick markings of black ink on Cheryl's chest, all the way up to her neck, and covered certain markings with bulky, uncomfortable tape which could not be removed for a month and a half. The markings identified the target zones, and the tape protected them from water damage or other erasure. The radiation therapy itself lasted four and a half weeks, from September 30 to October 29. The treatments ate up nearly half a day every weekday, even though the actual time "under the gun" at 8 am and 2 pm was only a matter of minutes. Cheryl has fair skin, and she very quickly developed a "sunburn" effect. She found relief with some pretty effective ointments, along with clippings from an Aloe Vera plant that she applied to the area at least twice a day.

During this period, we were able to secure some life insurance for Cheryl as a conversion of her work-related group policy. The price would not be considered cheap for a healthy person, and we would now have to pay the entire cost out-of-pocket, but it was certainly a bargain for someone with inflammatory breast cancer. Besides, I thought it would be a wise purchase as a precautionary measure, given the gravely uncertain circumstances we were facing. Cheryl, however, signed the papers "under protest." She intended to survive!

The twice-daily radiation was really tough. Cheryl's skin turned a brilliant red, but her resiliency was equal to the task. Aloe Vera has amazing curative properties, and her daily application of this and other concoctions was paying off. All of the nutrients from freshly juiced vegetables and apples probably did not hurt, either. In fact, the radiologist was getting frustrated that Cheryl was not red enough, so she counteracted with some stronger measures. By the time she was through, her skin was fried and tender. Finally, the last radiation treatment came on Friday afternoon, October 29. The nurses and receptionists were gearing up for a Halloween party, and we were ready to get out of there, as if the clinic were truly haunted. When Cheryl finally did a follow-up visit with the radiologist in late January 2005, the nurse beamed and said, "I'm happy to see you." Cheryl shot back, "I'm not happy to see you!" It was nothing personal, to be sure, but she did not want any part of that place.

Cheryl had weathered the storm of chemotherapy, followed almost immediately by disfiguring surgery, which in turn was followed almost right away by intense radiation. The eight months of treatment had taken their toll. That weekend, perhaps, it all caught up with her. She was as sick as a dog. I had canceled an out-of-state trip in which I was scheduled to speak on the subject of evangelism, and the timing of the cancellation could not have been better. Cheryl needed family support, and no "chemo brain" episodes would prevent it this time.

Two and a half weeks later, on Wednesday, November 17, Cheryl started a brief program of physical therapy which ended in late December. Her chest was still unusually tight from surgery, her right arm needed to be limbered up, and there was concern about possible swelling in the arm as a result of all the lymph nodes that had been removed. As it turned out, her right arm had swollen up a little, temporarily, but it may have been induced by all the radiation. The physical therapy loosened Cheryl up, helped her relax, and provided us with some lymph fluid drainage exercises, just in case lymphedema ever became a problem. She was beginning to limber up and heal, and she started feeling like her old self.

On December 1, she went to the dentist to complete some work which had been postponed for about nine months. The hygienist had never seen such healthy-looking teeth in a chemotherapy patient, and we attributed it to Cheryl's nutritional regimen. The dentist walked in and asked, "Can I take your cap off?" She replied, "Sure," thinking that was why she was there in the first place, to remove the temporary cap on her tooth and replace it with a permanent one. Then he proceeded to yank off her hat! Cheryl is not prone to relax in a dentist's office, as it ranks right up there with the radiology clinic on her list of least favorite places to go, but this time she burst out laughing.

Fortunately, by this point her hair had begun to grow back and there was something underneath that "cap."

Sermon Excerpt
"Becoming Better Husbands,"
preached on April 17, 2005

The most significant factor in any healthy relationship is *honor.* The most fundamental of all relationships is the one we must have with God. In Leviticus 10:3, the LORD says, "Among those who are near me I will be sanctified, and before all the people I will be glorified." The priests, Nadab and Abihu, failed to honor God when they offered "unauthorized fire," and they paid for it with their own lives. God will be honored, whether or not we choose to be part of the process. In like manner, by creating mankind in His own image and likeness, God crowned humanity "with glory and honor" (Psalm 8:5).

Honor also defines healthy interpersonal relationships on earth, and it is always a two-way street. Christians are to prefer one another in honor (Rom. 12:10). Children must honor their parents (Eph. 6:2). Fathers, in turn, are instructed not to "provoke your children, lest they become discouraged" (Col. 3:21). If parents do not learn to transmit Biblical principles in a way that honors the individuality of each child, then there is a greater likelihood of backlash rejection.

In the marriage relationship, wives must honor their husbands. *"Wives, submit to your own husbands, as to the Lord. For the husband is the head of the wife even as Christ is the head of the church, his body, and is himself its Savior. Now as the church submits to Christ, so also wives should submit in everything to their husbands"* (Eph. 5:22-24). Likewise, the apostle adds, *"Husbands, love your wives, as Christ loved the church and gave himself up for her, that he might sanctify her, having cleansed her by the washing of water with the word, so that he might present the church to himself in splendor, without spot or wrinkle or any such thing, that she might be holy and without blemish. In the same way husbands should love their wives as their own bodies. He who loves his wife loves himself. For no one ever hated his own flesh, but nourishes and cherishes it, just as Christ does the church"* (Eph. 5:25-29). Once again, honor flows both ways.

Men and women are different. There really is some truth to John Gray's Mars-Venus analogy. In sexual matters, men have a visual ignition switch, and women have one more tied to relational intimacy. As males and females, we are wired differently, we have different hormones, and we have different needs. Men, in honoring your wives, you must give her what *she* needs, not what you would like her to have.

More than anything else, it will likely be the honor of recognition of her worth and value. Someone has said, "Romance begins by exchanging sweet nothings and ends by saying nothing sweet." Our wives need frequent verbal affirmations from us, as well as actions that speak louder than words. You have to communicate to your wife, "You complete my circle and fill my emptiness." In so doing, you will put her on a pedestal of honor. Proverbs 31:28-30 says of the worthy woman, *"Her children rise up and call her blessed; her husband also, and he praises her: 'Many women have done excellently, but you surpass them all.' Charm is deceitful, and beauty is vain, but a woman who fears the LORD is to be praised."*

My own wife has experienced an emotional roller-coaster of life-threatening cancer, intolerable chemotherapy which took away her red hair, and disfiguring surgery. There are times when she feels anything but attractive. I suppose that some men, dominated by the flesh, would see such a wife as less than a whole person, to be discarded and traded in for someone else. To me, that would be unconscionable. I tell Cheryl that I love her, that she is still the most beautiful girl in the world to me, and that I'd marry her all over again. And I mean it!

Chapter 6

Family Bonding:
Dealing With the Kids

"And he will turn the hearts of fathers to their children and the hearts of children to their fathers, lest I come and strike the land with a decree of utter destruction." Malachi 4:6

One issue that arises for most cancer patients is how the disease will impact the rest of the family. When the diagnosis first hit, both of our daughters were devastated, and there was a lot of family crying. From our California days when the girls were young, Cheryl has a license plate frame which reads, "Final Score: Girls 2, Boys 0." We were blessed with two daughters, and so I have long been the "odd man out," even if I love my girls dearly. Nonetheless, whenever female hormones start flying around our house, I sometimes try to go find a quiet corner. In this case, we had to meet this challenge as a unified team.

Cheryl had no family history of breast cancer, and this disease caught her somewhat by surprise. Our two daughters, Megan and Brooke, will have to live with a little cloud over their heads. They will likely have to take some special precautions and develop healthy eating habits. In fact, Cheryl has continually pleaded with them to do so, almost nonstop, and some of her preaching appears to have taken root. With a mother's track record, they may be at greater risk of contracting breast cancer themselves. As a concerned husband and father who learned from experience, I will strongly advise them to go ahead and get a biopsy, rather than take a doctor's reassuring word for granted, if there are ever any suspicious symptoms.

Our daughters will also have to live the next few years not knowing if they will have a healthy mother. On one occasion, when one of the girls was moaning about all the presents a cousin had received for her birthday – things which we could not afford to provide – Cheryl unabashedly informed her, "Your birthday present this year is having a mother who's alive!" Needless to say, even though there were a few material presents as well, the statement put things into perspective. For her own part, Cheryl wanted very much to watch her children grow to womanhood, marry, and bear children. She wanted to be a grandmother one day.

Megan, Cheryl, Mike and Brooke

With Cheryl's activity severely restricted at times because of the treatment, Megan and Brooke had to help out around the house more than they ever had before. At mealtime, they often had to cook, at least if they wanted to eat, and high expectations were placed on them for cleaning up around the house. This was in addition to the busy school and part time job schedule they already had. Megan worked locally at a family-owned drugstore, and Brooke babysat almost every Saturday as well as some weeknights. Because of cancer-related financial pressures, they now had to purchase most of their clothing and personal items. Both girls are good students, and we are very proud of how responsible they have grown up to be. When cancer hit, they had to grow up even faster.

Obviously, there were some tense moments as the events unfolded. Both girls at times seemed to resent how much Cheryl and I would talk to others about the cancer and her regimen. It was good therapy for us, and people had a lot of questions, but the discussions confronted the girls with an unpleasant subject. As Megan said, "I don't want to think about my mom dying."

Even in the best of situations, teenage girls have to deal with their hormones and the unpleasant situations of life at the same time. Sometimes the pressures of Cheryl's illness pushed Megan and Brooke over the edge, to the point of tearful exasperation. I can remember Cheryl consoling one of them late one evening, saying, "It will be better in the morning. Everything is better in the morning."

Family getaways became even more important, both as a relief from pent-up stress as well for mutual support and bonding. Vance Havner, commenting on Mark 6:31, said, "If we didn't come apart and rest, we would just come apart." I previously mentioned some family trips taken even in between Cheryl's chemotherapy infusions. With all the precautionary measures we had to take, and the alternative dietary and medical paraphernalia Cheryl had to bring with her, those outings required a lot of planning and effort. We almost never regretted, however, the rest and relaxation that the time off afforded us. During a crisis, families sometimes pull away from each other, but we made some calculated efforts to draw closer together.

A few months after the diagnosis, a local spa sponsored a teen essay contest for the daughter of a worthy mother, who would get the royal treatment. Megan entered the contest, submitted an essay entitled "My Mother," and won. For about a month, Meg's name was blazoned across a sign outside the establishment, and in a small town like Trussville, it was big news among family and friends. This is what she wrote:

"Words cannot describe what I think about my mother. She has sacrificed for me and would give up her life for me. She is the best mother a daughter could ask for because of her endless love. Through her the Lord has richly blessed me.

"My mother is the most humble, generous woman I know. She has devoted her life to serving others. She is always thinking of others before herself. She cooks meals for the sick, sends cards to those who need encouragement, and is willing to drop anything she is doing if someone is in need.

"I want nothing more than to promise my mother that she has many years of joy awaiting her. She has recently been diagnosed with inflammatory breast cancer and the doctors are not making any promises due to the fact that this type of cancer is very dangerous. After her chemotherapy treatments nothing can seem to make my mother feel comfortable. I hate rubbing others' feet, but after I see the pain in her eyes I would give anything to make her pain go away, so I set aside my discomfort and rub her feet. Her scalp burns and her skin coloration is not normal. Yet instead of feeling sorry for herself, she still maintains her general perky, hopeful attitude.

*She takes one day at a time and says that she is choosing not
to be sick. She tells people that this is not really happening to
her, that it is just a bad dream.*

*"The reality of the matter is that life is short and that
everyone is going to die one day. However, my mom is
strong and can fight this. This year I would like nothing
better than my mother being pampered at a spa on Mother's
Day. She deserves it and I hope that you will consider her a
worthy winner of this contest."*

Needless to say, Cheryl and I were delighted to read such
sentiments from our firstborn daughter. The fact that she won
was a bonus. The pulling together of family in a time of
crisis is better medicine than any spa treatment in the world.
It is deeply satisfying to see many of Cheryl's traits resurfac-
ing in both daughters as they mature and grow spiritually.

Perhaps the toughest family issue during the first year
after diagnosis was whether Megan would enroll in August,
as planned, at Florida College, in Temple Terrace, Florida,
which is about 600 miles away. Cheryl and I are alumni of
this faith-based private institution, and it is in fact where we
met. Megan had long dreamed to go there as well, and
Cheryl, who had grown up just miles from FC, had in fact
pushed the idea from the time the girls were young. Given
the uncertainty of her short-term future, could this mother
part with her daughter? It is not Cheryl's nature to anticipate
such familial separations without excruciating emotion,
even without having to contend with cancer. The exacerbat-
ing circumstance on this particular occasion is that it came
just four days after her mastectomy. When all was said and
done, we let Megan go, with the proviso that she might have
to come home in case of an emergency or a severe turn for
the worse. Cheryl was thinking out loud, though, that it
might be "worse to lose a daughter than a breast!"

63

The Wilson "pirates" on vacation

Our younger daughter, Brooke, is full of spunk, personality, and a mind of her own. She is a good student, an outstanding cook, and a gifted singer. In fact, she twice made the state choir after we moved to Alabama. These are certainly endearing qualities, but Brooke has occasionally been known to be a *strong willed* child, with all the challenges that presents. It really is amazing how two kids born into the same family can be so entirely different from each other.

Brooke obtained her driving permit in December 2004. Independent of spirit, she quickly became a good driver, but the early efforts were a little interesting. After Grandpa Jack and I had taught her how to drive, Brooke was sometimes accompanied on these "test drives" by her mother. However, Cheryl quickly challenged me to carry my full part of the load, saying, "I think we need to take turns at this, because it's very stressful, and I don't want to grow cancer cells!"

In keeping with her temperament, Brooke held out and

was determined to become a Christian in her own time. By the time she was 15½ years old, we began to become more proactive in urging her to give her life to Christ, and the endless delay was killing us more than her driving was. Cheryl read Scripture with her twice weekly to help prepare her for her Bible lessons, making a few pointed applications along the way. I insisted on having a weekly Bible study with Brooke and was really struggling against my natural inclinations to push her too hard, because ultimately it was a decision she would have to make herself.

Finally, on February 27, 2005, I preached a sermon entitled, "Should You Wait?" As soon as everyone stood to sing the invitation song at the end, Brooke made a beeline toward me, along with her good friend, Laura Smith, and I gave them both a bear hug. A third young lady, Sara Cooley, followed behind. I'm not given to shedding as many tears as Cheryl is, but this moment was one of the proudest in my life. The three girls confessed their faith and were promptly baptized into Christ. Brooke's conversion was the most important "unfinished business" of Cheryl's life. Fortunately, there were new challenges to face now, and she still had much kingdom work to do.

Sermon Excerpt
"Should You Wait?" preached on February 27, 2005

Waiting is sometimes a necessary part of life. As the familiar saying goes, "Good things come to those who wait." *Perseverance* and *steadfast endurance* are positive virtues in the Bible, and impatient believers are counseled to *wait on the LORD*. There are times, however, when waiting is not such a good idea.

1. Should you wait to get involved? God wants us to be busy in His service. In Isaiah 6:8, Isaiah volunteers for service by saying, "Here am I! Send me." There are some areas of service that require years of preparation, but everyone can do something right now. Isaiah was moved by a sense of higher purpose, by a sense of duty. If you were to do a spiritual cost-benefit analysis, has the investment made in your spiritual development been matched by what you have given back? What about the time and opportunities the Lord has invested in you? Is that investment paying dividends? Are you a willing volunteer? Or have you simply been "choked by the cares and riches and pleasures of life" so that there is no productivity (Luke 8:14)? *What would God say?*

2. Should you wait to repent of sin? People play Russian Roulette with their souls. 2 Pet. 3:9-10 says, "The Lord is not slow to fulfill his promise as some count slowness, but is patient toward you, not wishing that any should perish, but that all should reach repentance. But the day of the Lord will come like a thief, and then the heavens will pass away with a roar, and the heavenly bodies will be burned up and dissolved...." Governor Felix waited for a more convenient "opportunity" to consider the coming judgment, and it evidently never came (Acts 24:24-25). Do you have sin in your life and a need for repentance? *What would God say?*

3. Should you wait to obey the gospel? Some young people are not mature enough to respond to the gospel, but others just pile up excuses. There are those who say they are "not convinced," just like the rich man who ended up in torment (Lk. 16:27-31). Others claim they "don't know enough," even when opportunities to know the truth of God exist all around them. Ephesians 4:18 warns against willful ignorance. Still others are afraid of the commitment. Like the one-talent man in Jesus' parable, the fear of failure paralyzes them and they bury their opportunity. Some people live in self-denial, saying to themselves, "I'm not a bad person," even thought the Bible says, "For all have sinned and fall short of the glory of God" (Rom. 3:23). Others convince themselves that they are just "not ready" to live the Christian life, even though God has promised us, "'I will never leave you nor forsake you.' So that we can confidently say, 'The Lord is my helper; I will not fear...'" (Heb. 13:5-6). Finally, there are those who speak of obeying the Lord "one of these days." They need to be reminded that "the road to hell is paved with good intentions." If you want to be eternally lost, then all you have to do is nothing. Do you need to obey the gospel? *What would God say?*

A few years ago there was a very talented basketball player at Oregon State University. He had a rare heart irregularity, and a reporter asked him about it. He said, "I'm not worried about nothing. I'm young." A week later, he collapsed in cardiac arrest and died.

It's hard to understand the thought process of those who delay doing what they know they need to do. "One of these days I'm going to get busy in the Lord's service... One of these days I'm going to repent of my sins... One of these days I'm going to going to take spiritual things more seriously... One of these days I'm going to obey the gospel... One of these days I'm going to quit this nonsense and get serious!"

One of these days doesn't cut it, if you need to come to terms with God *now!*

Chapter 7

Surprises from Spiritual Family

"Let love be genuine. Abhor what is evil; hold fast to what is good. Love one another with brotherly affection. Outdo one another in showing honor. Do not be slothful in zeal, be fervent in spirit, serve the Lord. Rejoice in hope, be patient in tribulation, be constant in prayer. Contribute to the needs of the saints and seek to show hospitality." Romans 12:9-13

"By this all people will know that you are my disciples, if you have love for one another." John 13:35

In this book I have made use of our experiences with Cheryl's illness as representative of the thought process of all faithful Christians who are diagnosed with life-threatening cancer. This is not to suggest that any two cases of the disease are exactly alike, or that the decision-making process regarding treatment is always the same. I am merely suggesting that Christians have a distinct advantage over unbelievers in dealing with a health crisis. One of the greatest blessings is the community of support found in the family of God.

Dealing with cancer can be a lonely undertaking. No one really enjoys the challenge. On several occasions, Cheryl quipped, "I've decided that cancer is overrated. I'm over it!" To her, the whole experience was "like a bad dream, as if it were happening to someone else." Several people felt very uncomfortable around her, not knowing quite how to react or what to say. Cheryl has a natural gift of putting people at ease, but she does not like to be the center of attention, much less be totally avoided as if she has the plague. When chemotherapy had taken away her hair, she would even make a game of it, as if turnabout is fair play, sneaking a peek at others when they least expected it. On one occasion, while at the store, she happened to notice a man, head turned, so mesmerized by her chemo-induced baldness that he ran into some shopping carts.

Immediately after the diagnosis, support came from almost everywhere. Cheryl was teaching at Bright Horizons preschool at the time, and other teachers sent home a huge banner with tiny, painted hand-prints all over it, with the message, "We Love You, Ms. Cheryl." It ran the length of our bedroom, and Cheryl, determined to surround herself with positive messages, left it hanging for months. Neighbors expressed concern, and one next-door neighbor showed extraordinary kindness, bringing some food and other gifts. There were visits from extended family members and good friends from the west coast, like Dina Masters-Graham and Jennifer Strutz, who came to help around the house and meet some of our needs. A psychologist friend kept his head shaved while Cheryl was on chemo.

By far and away, the most unexpected support came from God's people both locally and all over the world. We knew as the crisis began that we would receive some help from brothers and sisters in Christ. Moreover, as a preacher of the gospel, I have taken great comfort from Jesus' words in Mark 10:29-30 – *"Truly, I say to you, there is no one who has left*

*house or brothers or sisters or mother or father or children or
lands, for my sake and for the gospel, who will not receive a
hundredfold now in this time, houses and brothers and sisters
and mothers and children and lands, with persecutions, and
in the age to come eternal life."* Our family has lived those
words, and Alabama is not the native home of either Cheryl
or me. We have grown to love the people and the natural
beauty of this state, but we had lived in Alabama only a year
and a half when the bad news hit. I am a Californian, Cheryl
is a Floridian, and our respective families are concentrated in
those states. We have no extended family anywhere near
Birmingham. While we halfway expected our "spiritual
family" to make up for the lack of physical family in close
proximity, we were totally unprepared for either the level or
the intensity of the support we received.

First, we were literally inundated with cards, calls,
emails, flowers, and gifts from many states as well as a few
foreign countries. I have done temporary preaching assign-
ments with churches in about 20 states, as well as local
established work with congregations in California and
Oregon, before moving to Alabama, so we know a lot of
Christians across the country. For several months, our mailbox was completely stuffed every day with beautiful cards
and kind sentiments. We could barely read all the emails
and cards, let alone reply. I felt sorry for the mail carrier
who had our route!

There was much encouragement in these messages. Dee
Bowman urged us to remember that "God is on the throne.
And He will hear." Jill Bell wrote, "My hope for you is *life!*"
She sent a card with a little lamb to remind Cheryl "of the
Good Shepherd who cradles you moment by moment in the
shelter of His bosom. Take refuge, as Elijah did in times of
trouble, in the comfort and protection of the Almighty God,
your Abba. Grace and peace be yours in profuse abundance!
Just wanted you to know you're loved... and appreciated...

and adored... and cared for... and thought of... and lifted up by holy hands in prayer as a sweet aroma to the throne." Sewell Hall confided to me, "Caneta and I mention her almost every day in our prayers to God. He is able to do 'exceedingly abundantly above all that we ask or think.' Faith is a wonderful possession in such times. We are thankful that she has responded as well as she has to the treatment." Don Alexander wrote, "Peggy and I pray daily for Cheryl and for your whole family. May the Lord bless you and keep you, cause his face to shine upon you, and give you peace." When news of the cancer first hit, several people expressed shock, grief, or heavy hearts. Just knowing that others were hurting with us, even from a distance, was a great comfort. Most of all, spiritual brothers and sisters told us they were praying for us, both privately and publicly. The Lord only knows how many tens of thousands of prayers went up, but I am sure from the correspondence we received that heaven was bombarded. (See Appendix 4, A Sister's Prayer).

Cheryl saved the cards and printed emails in a couple of large boxes, and as we were going through them over a year later, we were reminded of this overwhelming show of love. Several people, including Cathy Kinser of California, sent what seemed like several cards a week. Jean King, a local sister, mailed a steady stream of cards with little surprises in them. We especially appreciated the illustrated love notes from young children. Total strangers sent cards and care packages. Several ladies' Bible class groups, including some who were unknown to us by face, sent boxes full of thoughtful tokens. Every day there was a new adventure waiting for us at the mailbox or front door, and we were humbled by the kindness of our fellow Christians.

The local congregation of which we are a part mobilized for action and showed us more Southern hospitality than we ever could have imagined. When Cheryl was flat on her back with chemo, several ladies of the Edward's Lake church took turns bringing us dinner for what seemed like a couple of months. Given my wife's unusual dietary requirements – since she was virtually a vegetarian already – these dear sisters in Christ went out of their way to purchase fresh, organic fruits and vegetables especially for her. Megan, Brooke and I were not entirely disabled at the time, but these women insisted on bringing us food. At times when Cheryl felt somewhat better, we had to be adamant that they stop this generosity and allow us to prepare our own meals.

Our local network of support did not stop with food. A ladies' group gathered together on a Saturday just to pray for Cheryl, and they put pictures of their smiling faces on the outside of a customized tote bag that Cheryl used to transport personal items to medical appointments. These same women were involved in the "hat incident" mentioned earlier. On one occasion, Cheryl and I came back from the doctor's office, and a whole army of Christians had done some major yard work. On another occasion, after a family vacation, we came back to a clean house. There was a steady supply of gifts, expressions of concern, and many heartfelt prayers offered on our behalf by members of the Edward's Lake Church of Christ. There were also monetary gifts, but that will occupy a separate chapter. It is an amazing thing to be part of a local church family in which so many saints demonstrate the love of God in their personal lives. Just thinking about these wonderful people puts a smile on the face and reinforces a strong desire to rid the body of unwanted cancer cells. Cheryl did not think too much about joining a "support group" because she already had more support than any reasonable person could ever expect.

The five elders of the church truly acted as spiritual shepherds throughout this ordeal. Keith Poe and Chris Ellis said beautiful prayers, Joel Ellis helped me to keep my optimism and focus, and Ralph Scott declared Cheryl as an adopted daughter. As for Richard Buchanan, there were moments when he was prone to buttress our spirits in a public way. He is the one who led the song, "God will take care of you," prior to the surgery, as mentioned previously. On another occasion, he was giving some general announcements and read Isaiah 44:5 to the assembly. The passage says, "This one will say, 'I am the LORD's,' another will call on the name of Jacob, and another will write on his hand, 'The LORD's,' and name himself by the name of Israel." Richard then lifted up his hand and said, "This may be kind of corny, but I have written Cheryl's name on my hand." Corny or not, we appreciated the sentiments.

Who ever said kind words do not have an impact on someone's well-being? Jay Hunt, an older brother in Christ who had health issues of his own, was especially full of encouragement. He confided to me, "I've thought all along she's going to be completely healed of this. If she has any negative thoughts, you tell her to get rid of them right away!" We will never be able to forget Mildred Jernigan's prayer that Cheryl would be spared and she would be taken. Mildred was not the only Christian friend who passed away during this period. Bob Barton, Richard Copeland, Phil Roberts, Thelma West and other esteemed saints who had specifically prayed for Cheryl completed their earthly walk even as her own health appeared to improve. At Richard's funeral Cheryl remarked, "There's no cancer in heaven."

Sermon Excerpt
"Reaching out to the Lost," preached on March 6, 2005

What is the mission of the local church? I have used the following terms to help local Christians keep their collective focus:

1) **Unify** – relationship in God's family. This involves integrating new members and striving for the unity of the faith together (I Cor. 1:10; Eph. 4:13);
2) **Edify** – growth in God's school. This encompasses discipleship and follow-up teaching (Eph. 4:13; 2 Tim. 2:2; 2 Pet. 3:18);
3) **Glorify** – access to God's throne. Christians are recipients of a great gift, the opportunity to come before God in worship (Acts 2:42; Eph. 3:14-21);
4) **Supply** – usefulness in God's service. This involves meeting other Christians' needs in benevolent ministry (Eph. 4:12; 1 Pet. 4:11-12);
5) **Multiply** – sharing of God's salvation; i.e., evangelizing the lost (Mt. 28:18-20; Rom. 1:16).

Each of these roles contains an inherent benefit. In a congregation of authentic Christians, one can build relationships with wonderful people of God (fellowship), take advantage of the finest personal development opportunity (discipleship), participate in the greatest privilege (worship), exercise the most valuable use of his talents and resources (service), and get involved in the world's greatest cause (evangelism). If people fully realized what we have, in this unique spiritual relationship, they would break down the doors trying to get in! God has granted to us an "inexpressible gift" (2 Cor. 9:15), but perhaps we need to learn how to articulate the benefits to others and *connect* with them. If this were a corporate business – which it is not – it would be like having the greatest product in the world while not having a clue how to market it. How can we become "all things to all people" in an effort to win them to Christ (1 Cor. 9:22)?

People are lost in sin and need a Savior. Sometimes, however, Jesus concentrated on the self-perceived needs of His audience as a gateway to serving their greatest need. For example, He asks a blind man, "What do you want me to do for you?" (Mark 10:51). While we should never interpret this as an excuse for compromising the scriptural blueprint and turning the church into something it is not, there is certainly a valuable lesson Jesus can teach us in this regard. What are people's self-perceived needs today? They are hurting and lonely, and they sense a need for healthy relationships. They are in a rut, and they need personal development. They are disadvantaged and need access. They are underappreciated and underutilized, and they yearn for a sense of usefulness. They are aimless and need a worthy cause.

Where can they find these things? In Christ and the church! Perhaps we ought to help them make the connection:

1) **Unify** – relationship with God and His family (i.e., no more isolation);
2) **Edify** – the greatest personal development (i.e., no more spiritual ignorance);
3) **Glorify** – the greatest privilege (i.e., no more barriers);
4) **Supply** – the greatest use of one's God-given abilities (i.e., no more insignificance);
5) **Multiply** – the greatest cause (i.e., no more purposelessness).

A congregation modeled after the Biblical pattern is a unique relationship of people who have been saved by the blood of Christ and who are doing the Lord's work together locally. They sing together, pray together, pull for one another, and help each other in their struggles. Even though we will be individually judged, in many respects *no one goes to heaven alone.*

Chapter 8

Financial Challenges: "Windows of Heaven"

"Bring the full tithes into the storehouse, that there may be food in my house. And thereby put me to the test, says the LORD of hosts, if I will not open the windows of heaven for you and pour down for you a blessing until there is no more need." Malachi 3:10

Financial advisors sometimes warn that the average American family is one health crisis away from financial disaster. When a serious case of cancer strikes, it hits hard. There are so many dimensions to it, causing family life to suffer a complete upheaval. Affected areas, besides the physical wellness of the victim, may include, but are not limited to, emotional stability, sexual relations, work life, family relationships, long-range planning, and potential financial ruin. There are multiple tensions that must be dealt with simultaneously.

I am a preacher, and, like many preachers, have made some financial sacrifices to bypass a career in the business world. For the most part, churches that have supported my efforts have been thoughtful and generous. In nearly 25 years of fulltime preaching, there has been only one brief instance in which I believe I was severely underpaid. Nevertheless, as is the case for many of my partners in the pulpit, a large portion of my "salary" has actually been allocated for unreimbursed, work-related expenses as well as for fringe benefits that many in the secular workplace take for granted. Consequently, even though our family has enjoyed a comfortable lifestyle, all in all, we never had a tremendous amount of breathing room financially. It is a small sacrifice to pay for the privilege and honor of speaking "the unsearchable riches of Christ," and I was well aware of the challenge when I decided to devote my life to this work many years ago.

Through the years, Cheryl has made some huge sacrifices of her own. Although trained and licensed as a teacher, she has not held a position in the public school system since before we were married. Instead, she is a committed mother who takes pride in the time she has given to our kids. Moreover, she takes very seriously her Biblical role as manager of the household (I Tim. 5:14; Tit. 2:5). However, like the "excellent wife" of Proverbs 31, she has also on occasion worked part time outside the home in order to supply the needs of our daughters and others. We spent 16 years in hyper-expensive Orange County of southern California, and she operated her own housecleaning business for several of those years, without sacrificing the priority of motherhood in the process.

About a year before her cancer diagnosis, Cheryl started working at a preschool. The job provided some much-needed funds for retirement savings, gifts, and other assorted expenses, but the primary purpose was to help finance our girls' college education. We wanted to assist them in going to Florida College, a private institution with emphasis on Biblical values, without piling up massive debt. Over the years, we had been able to put away a few dollars for this purpose, and the girls themselves had saved a certain amount of money, but tuition costs had soared and totally dwarfed our family budget. We had hoped that Cheryl's job would make up the deficit.

Cancer not only put a quick halt to those plans, but we were suddenly confronted with a triple whammy of potential red ink. First, Megan was six months away from her first college semester, and we were a long way from meeting the goal for educational savings. Second, even with fairly good health insurance, there would most certainly be some massive medical bills. Third, in order to give Cheryl the best chance for survival, we soon committed to an alternative regimen to complement conventional treatment, but the expense for this alone would regularly exceed $1,000 a month. The costs in this last category are not covered by medical insurance, and are mostly not even tax deductible. Additionally, there would be some *hidden* costs, including enormous expenses for Cheryl's special diet. The cumulative effect of dealing with these budgetary pressures gave me a headache. At one point, overwhelmed with tension, even Cheryl cried out, "You could have done anything with your life! Why do we have to struggle like this?"

In money matters, people have a tendency to depend upon human solutions instead of God. While taking charge of personal finances is a good thing, too much self-reliance can lead to ingratitude toward our Eternal Giver. In the movie, *Shenandoah,* Jimmy Stewart plays the part of a Virginia farmer who tries to perpetuate in a non-religious way the Christian memory of his dearly departed wife. He prays, "Lord, we cleared this land, we plowed it, sowed it, and harvested. We cooked the harvest. It wouldn't be here, and we wouldn't be eatin' it, if we hadn't done it all ourselves. We worked dog-bone hard for every crumb and morsel, but we thank you just the same anyway, Lord, for this food we're about to eat. Amen."

Even Christians sometimes lapse into a do-it-yourself independence that forgets the element of divine blessing. Watchman Nee of China challenged this assumption when he said, "Many of us only expect results commensurate with what we are in ourselves, but blessing is fruit that is out of all correspondence with what we are. It is not just the working of cause and effect, for when we reckon on the basis of what we put in we merely bar the way for God to work beyond our reckoning."[1] God can open "windows of heaven" and bless us beyond our wildest imaginations, if we put Him first in our lives. In Deuteronomy 28, God says that He will "command the blessing on you" (v. 8), and that His blessings will "overtake you" (v. 2).

Cheryl and I determined therefore to put our faith in God, and, in a sense, to put Him to the test in the best spirit of Malachi 3:10. Some intense prayers were said, for financial stability in addition to Cheryl's recovery. Under an avalanche of that kind of pressure, there is a natural tendency to cut back in all areas of a budget, but there is one area in this "test" that was non-negotiable. Even though Cheryl was suddenly out of work, we would not lower our weekly contribution check in support of the Lord's work. If I recall, we actually *raised* it slightly at the time. Would we be buried financially? Would we have to sell the house? Where in the world was needed money going to come from?

As events unfolded, we were able to handle the unforeseen load in remarkable ways, through a series of extraordinary *coincidences.* I have never experienced anything quite like it in my life. Even though some of this is quite personal, I feel it must be shared, in light of the overall message of the book.

First, Cheryl's preschool had a contract to service the needs of Blue Cross-Blue Shield of Alabama, and all the kids in Cheryl's preschool were children of Blue Cross employees. Since our health insurance just happened to be with the same company, several of the parents told her that if she ever had a billing problem to just give them a call, and they would look into it. In the months that followed, we never added up the combined costs of Cheryl's chemotherapy, surgery, and radiation treatments, but I believe that the total bill was probably at least $200,000. We were out-of-pocket several thousand dollars, but our medical insurance took care of the rest, and we never had a billing discrepancy. I doubt we received any special treatment, but there may have been some insiders making sure our case was handled properly, and it was nice to know that we had some connections if a problem ever came up.

Another pleasant turn of events developed as a result of a decision we made just two or three months prior to the diagnosis. Late in 2003, Cheryl was presented the opportunity to purchase job-related disability insurance. We were unsure about it, and had no idea it would cover an unforeseen cancer-related catastrophe, but as the cost was only a few dollars a month, we shrugged and opted to do it. Little did we know at the time how much we would need it! Shortly after Cheryl started on chemotherapy, she started to receive short-term benefits, which were later converted into long-term benefits. About five months into treatment, she applied for Social Security disability, which was likewise granted. I have heard horror stories from other worthy individuals who fought hard and were sometimes denied private and government-sponsored disability benefits. We felt very blessed that this process went so smoothly for us and that this kind of help was even available. With the waiting periods and reduced income-percentages factored in, the disability payments did not by any means compensate for the loss of Cheryl's income, but they did cover much of her alternative medical expenses, at least for a time.

As for Megan's college bill, she received a couple of

totally unexpected scholarships. Additionally, Florida College has an Adopt-a-Student program in which donors help certain students with tuition payments. We applied for it, and five families or individuals quickly lined up to contribute to her first year of schooling. One was a dear Christian couple in North Carolina. The others all belonged to the Edward's Lake church in Birmingham. I am not certain that any of them gave "out of their abundance." In fact, two of the donors were living off of retirement incomes. Two other providers lost their jobs shortly after donating. All of this was a catalyst for prayer, both for thanksgiving and for God to return the blessing. We especially prayed hard for one brother who had trouble replacing his job, since we felt we had a vested interest in his success. Tuition, room and board for Megan's first year of college totaled around $16,000, but the lion's share of the bill was paid for by others.

Truly, money for family needs came virtually out of nowhere, including some totally bizarre situations. For example, in September 2004 I was presenting a series of sermons for a church in the New Orleans area, and Hurricane Ivan preempted half the meeting. As the local preacher, Jeff Carr, transported me to the airport a couple of days early, people were leaving in droves and New Orleans seemed almost like a ghost town. Ironically, I flew back to Birmingham, which was hit almost directly by what was left of the storm, while New Orleans was spared. Our home suffered some damage, as water poured in from our dining room ceiling. We had buckets stationed everywhere to collect the drainage! A few days later, an insurance adjuster presented me a check for over $1,000 and told us to hire a contractor of our own choosing to do the work. We had a relatively new house, and I had previously contacted the homebuilder about the problem. Unfortunately, our one-year home warranty had expired, so the decision to make an insurance claim was well justified. The builder, however, came to check the situation out shortly thereafter. He must have felt sorry for us and arranged to send some sub-contractors to do all the interior work. I urged him to bill me for their work and he agreed to do it, but he had a benevolent spirit and the invoice never came. Richard Buchanan helped me with some minor repairs on the exterior of the house, so the actual repair costs were minimal. The surplus money was totally unforeseen, arrived just in time to pay some bills, and was put to good use.

Individuals must have sensed our need, and several people helped us out with a gift of cash or an unexpected check. A few close friends included a little gift when they sent a card urging Cheryl to get well. Cheryl's parents helped out with the purchase of a cancer-fighting supplement that cost $10 a day, and they made sure Megan's needs were taken care of as her first year of college approached. A couple of Christian families pitched in to buy me a notebook computer to aid my preaching work. The thoughts of this book came together on that computer screen. An older couple received a cash gift from a relative, and they shared a generous portion of it with us, on the grounds that *true blessings must be "shared"*!

Other examples of generosity could be given, but the bottom line is that every little bit added up. All of our needs were met in abundance as we continually defied the law of gravity. Through all these extraordinary circumstances, *Someone* was watching out for us. God used benevolent individuals, bizarre events, and unforeseen disability benefits to provide for the Wilson family. I could not quantify it if I had to do so, but at the end of Cheryl's first year with cancer, we were arguably in slightly better shape financially than we were at the start of the year, and we were abundantly rich with dear friends and divine blessings. Jesus promises, "But seek first the kingdom of God and his righteousness, and all these things will be added to you" (Matthew 6:33). I believe Him! Throughout this ordeal, God opened the "windows of heaven."

Sermon Excerpt
"The Boomerang Effect," preached on January 26, 2003

J. Hudson Taylor remarked, "When God's work is done in God's way for God's glory, it will never lack God's supply." Sometimes God uses *people like you* – something you say or do that sets into motion a chain reaction of blessing. Three times in 2 Corinthians Paul alludes to Christians taking the first step of a chain reaction that can actually have a *boomerang* effect, with the result that thanksgiving is offered to God for those who took the initial action.

1. Generosity. In 2 Corinthians 9:11-12, Paul speaks of the gift the Christians in Corinth were sending to the impoverished church at Jerusalem. He says, *"You will be enriched in every way for all your generosity, which through us will produce thanksgiving to God. For the ministry of this service is not only supplying the needs of the saints, but is also overflowing in many thanksgivings to God."* Generous giving involves expenditure, but it is also an investment. Having one's name mentioned by a grateful recipient in thanksgiving to God is not a matter to be taken lightly. Heaven does not soon forget that kind of acknowledgment. Jesus says, *"Give, and it will be given to you. Good measure, pressed down, shaken together, running over, will be put into your lap. For with the measure you use it will be measured back to you"* (Lk. 6:38). Divine blessings are a value-added benefit that cannot be quantified. I have come to the conclusion that anything worth having is worthy giving away. Do you want to be appreciated? Then show your appreciation for others, and it will return to you. Do you need more friends? Be a friend. Do you want more abundance in your life? Then share what you have with others. This is certainly true of the financial sacrifices we make in the name of Christ, because God instituted the law of sowing and reaping, and that law applies to generosity in giving.

2. Prayer. In 2 Corinthians 1:11, Paul makes a special request: *"You also must help us by prayer, so that many will give thanks on our behalf for the blessing granted us through the prayers of many."* Intercessory prayer can itself set off a chain reaction of blessing. Prayer is a catalyst because it changes things. Heaven responds, angels are sent, and blessings are granted. There is a return on investment in the form of thanksgivings offered to God by the recipients of the blessings instigated by the prayers of others. Have you ever noticed how openly Paul expresses his gratitude for the recipients of his letters? When we tell others we have mentioned their names in thanksgiving to Almighty God, their spirits are lifted. Can you think of a greater gift that you can give another Christian than to thank God for him, and then tell him about it?

3. Evangelism. In 2 Corinthians 4:15, Paul says, *"For it is all for your sake, so that as grace extends to more and more people it may increase thanksgiving, to the glory of God."* In the context of this statement, the apostle has alluded to his unbeatable spirit: "We are afflicted in every way, but not crushed; perplexed, but not driven to despair; persecuted, but not forsaken; struck down, but not destroyed" (4:8-9). He had experienced great adversity, but he would not allow it to defeat him. The gospel of Christ saves people from eternal doom, and for the benefit of others Paul would press on. What happens when lost people, like the Ethiopian eunuch, respond to the gospel in belief and baptism, and go on their way rejoicing (Acts 8:39)? If they truly appreciate what they have in Christ, they will give thanks! The cycle of blessing boomerangs. Imagine a grateful recipient of salvation thanking you for pointing him in the right direction and saying, "How can I ever repay you?" My response is, "Now go help someone else. You must share a generous portion of what you have received."

---

[1] Angus Kinnear, *The Story of Watchman Nee: Against the Tide* (Wheaton, IL: Tyndale House, 1978), p. 255

Chapter 9

Going "Alternative"

"In the thirty-ninth year of his reign Asa was diseased in his feet, and his disease became severe. Yet even in his disease he did not seek the LORD, but sought help from physicians." 2 Chronicles 16:12

From the very beginning of Cheryl's cancer experience, I waded through volumes of material, searching for the best natural remedies to complement conventional treatment. Such approaches are referred to as *complementary* therapy when mainstream treatment is accepted. They become *alternative* therapy when conventional approaches are largely rejected. Lee and Sally Vaughan, some close friends on the west coast, had sent us some videos by Dr. Lorraine Day, who had beaten breast cancer using alternative methods. Dr. Day's presentations are impressive, so we started implementing many of her strategies, even while we continued mainstream therapy at UAB. At the time, we wanted the best of both worlds.

During Cheryl's initial foray into the world of chemotherapy, surgery and radiation, she gravitated rather quickly to a mostly vegetarian diet, and she also took fistfuls of vitamins and herbs known for their cancer-fighting or immune-building properties. Ironically, doctors suggested that she continue eating meat, since protein intake will partially counterbalance the weakening effects of chemo. Likewise, the use of supplements is strongly discouraged by many physicians during chemotherapy and radiation, on the grounds that it will interfere with the treatment. Several studies, however, convinced me that this fear is not entirely justified. (See, for example, the Internet article by Dr. Michael T. Murray cited in Appendix 1). Cheryl's doctors were not totally *down* on vitamins, but her first oncologist suggested unconvincingly that most of what she was taking "will only make you a little poorer." We strongly disagreed. As far as we were concerned, chemotherapy is known to severely weaken the immune system, the body's primary defense against cancer, precisely at a time when the body needs it the most. Cheryl's radiologist tried to convince us to stay away from antioxidants, but she admitted that current research was not conclusive on the matter. We stuck to our guns.

Two factors in particular pushed us toward alternative approaches, especially as her core therapy at UAB was coming to an end. First, we wanted to take a more proactive approach rather than sit back and let nature take its course. Inflammatory breast cancer is difficult enough to beat, even with the finest medical care, and we wanted to give Cheryl every possible advantage. Second, conventional approaches do not have the best track record of beating this particular disease. Theologically, I am not one who believes that faith in God cancels out advances in modern medical science, or that Christians ought to reject all doctors and just pray for a miracle. After all, Luke, the companion of the apostle Paul, was a doctor! Dependence on God and human instrumentality are not mutually exclusive. I do believe, however, that much of the mainstream cancer industry is going down the wrong path, and my reasons for reaching this conclusion will be developed in the next chapter. The bottom line in this particular case is that Cheryl quickly exhausted most of her mainstream options and was still left with a "high probability" of recurrence. There was nothing more the UAB physicians offered her except Tamoxifen or similar drugs. We did not like the odds or the treatment limitations being presented.

Much of what we were doing *on the side* was somewhat random and haphazard, a hodgepodge of whatever research and respected advice we were able to collect on our own. I had thought about sending Cheryl to an alternative cancer clinic, but she would have had to leave home for an extended period of time, and the whole enterprise would have been cost prohibitive. We yearned for some professional help by a respected healthcare practitioner who was not given to fringe-element quackery, who had a history of stellar results, and who was able to think *outside the box* regarding treatment options. When Barry and Sarah Fultz moved from Tennessee to Alabama in mid-2004 and became part of the Edward's Lake church family, we finally had a connection to just the sort of person we were looking for.

Barry, Sandlyn and Sarah Fultz

Sandlyn Fulz, their daughter, had become gravely ill with kidney problems about the time of her second birthday, in late-September 1999. Tests at Vanderbilt Children's Hospital revealed a "spot." When examining the films, Sarah asked where exactly the spot was, and she was shown a huge area that occupied Sandlyn's entire pelvic region, from hip to hip. Some *spot!* It turned out to be an 8 centimeter cube. On October 8, she underwent emergency surgery, since the tumor had completely shut off her colon and stretched her urinary tract. The surgeons did a colostomy but warned that the tumor was likely wrapped around Sandlyn's spine, and that she would "probably never walk again."

A biopsy confirmed that Sandlyn had *rhabdomyosarcoma,* a rare, childhood cancer that likely originated in her uterus or bladder. She started chemotherapy and essentially lived in the hospital with her mother for the next seven months. On May 9, 2000, she had surgery to remove what was left of the tumor. In the process, surgeons did a partial hysterectomy and removed all of her uterus, one-third of her bladder and vagina, and half of her ureter. They also reconstructed her kidney.

A week later, the doctors informed Sandlyn's parents that they were not able to get all the cancer and that some remained on the pelvic wall. They suggested that the only option, in addition to five more months of chemotherapy already scheduled, was radiation. The downside was that the radiologist did not believe Sandlyn would survive the therapy. If she did manage to stay alive, the treatment would prevent her pelvis from ever fully developing, it would completely destroy her colon, bladder and ovaries, and there would be a good chance her legs would never grow again. If she were to survive radiation, which was unlikely, long-term survival would be only 20%. On the other hand, without radiation, the Fultzes were given no chance at all. They decided that quality of life was more important than facing all the horrors presented, especially with so little chance of survival. Sandlyn finished out the five additional months of chemo, but there would be no radiation.

In October, Barry and Sarah were thinking about scheduling a Make-A-Wish Foundation trip to Disney World the following March, but the oncologist urged them to "take it right now." He said that when they came back for a follow-up appointment in January, Sandlyn's cancer would have already relapsed and be full-blown. The family took the trip to Orlando in mid-October.

Later that month, they decided to drive several hours to an alternative health clinic in North Carolina. Sarah had been reading about alternative therapies and had heard some promising things about this clinic. The first order of business was a computerized test in order to determine comprehensively how Sandlyn's various body systems were functioning. Sarah recalls how she had never experienced anything quite like it, as results showed several specific deficiencies that needed to be addressed. One glitch, however, kept coming up on the test, and the administrator thought it was a computer error. He had never seen a child test positive for an adenovirus that continually registered for Sandlyn. What he did not know at the time is that the Vanderbilt system had detected the same adenovirus the previous March! The only difference is that at Vanderbilt, the test results took awhile to process and the family was not informed for 30 days. In this instance, the results were instantaneous. Sarah recalls, "At that point I knew this was not just a bunch of voodoo." Sandlyn started an intense nutritional regimen that included supplements which targeted specific deficiencies, a lot of juicing, and a strict diet.

About six months later, the family switched to a clinic closer to home, in middle Tennessee. The man who ran it, Dr. Larry Rawdon, was an alternative-minded pharmacist and licensed nutritional counselor. He had the same philosophies as the people in North Carolina, offered many of the same supplements, and kept Sandlyn on a similar regimen. The only difference is that he gauged Sandlyn's body systems with kinesiology, pH tests, and other methods without the aid of an expensive computerized system. Kinesiology uses the response of muscles when gently tested to find imbalances which interfere with optimum function. His findings for Sandlyn were less comprehensive, but virtually identical, to the test results in North Carolina.

In spite of the odds given by mainstream doctors, Sandlyn thrived. Her growth was stunted somewhat because of the terrible effects of year-long chemotherapy on a two-year old. Moreover, when she was hospitalized at Vanderbilt, she typically vomited 20 times a day, so an external feeding tube had been surgically placed into her stomach. Consequently, much of her fresh juice intake for the next several years was inserted through this tube. Years went by and the family waited breathlessly for the results of every cancer checkup. The Vanderbilt oncologist, no doubt certain that the cancer would return, insisted on a follow-up scan every six months. He disdainfully asked Sarah if Sandlyn was still taking "all those vitamins." By the time the Fultzes moved to the Birmingham area, Sandlyn was clear of cancer for over four years, and there was no sign of it coming back.

Sandlyn Fultz, an amazing success story

When Sarah Fultz heard of Cheryl's plight, she offered to escort us on a three-and-a-half hour trip from Birmingham to Hohenwald, Tennessee. Cheryl mispronounced it as "hole-in-wall" at first, but it is actually a delightful town with an amazing health clinic. We were cautiously optimistic and somewhat apprehensive, but we had nothing to lose. The initial trip took place August 30, while Cheryl was still in the middle of UAB treatment. This occurred only 14 days after her surgery. She was still suffering from the aftereffects of chemo, was totally bald, and had drainage tubes coming out of her chest – anything but the picture of perfect health! In fact, the very next day we would meet with the radiologist for the first time, with the start of radiation not far off. With regard to treatment choices, we had one foot planted at UAB and another planted in Tennessee.

We spent what seemed like half a day at the clinic. A Lorraine Day video was playing in the lobby, so we knew were in familiar territory right off. After the appropriate introductions, the same man who had worked with Sandlyn now collected background information and analyzed Cheryl's systemic deficiencies. Her pulse was high, her urine pH was extremely low, and there were evidences of several imbalances as well as parasite problems. He analyzed her blood-oxygen level. To help her skin heal up, some *light therapy* was used near the site of the mastectomy incision. Cheryl, never missing an opportunity for humor, asked, "Will it grow a new one?"

Dr. Rawdon is more of an educator than a medical doctor. *Doctor* comes from a Latin word meaning "teacher," so this is fitting. In any case, it quickly became apparent that he had something very substantial to offer us. His basic approach is to educate clients on how to take charge of their own health. With a substantial background in both pharmacy and naturopathy, his knowledge of the chemistry of nutrition and the body's internal healing system proved to be nothing short of encyclopedic.

Dr. Rawdon's basic premise was that life is a gift from God, and that the body works well when it functions according to the way it was designed. He showed us a clock running on the energy of an apple. Our consultant then began a brief lecture about the effects of *life energy* on bodily health. He suggested that God makes this life energy available in the air we breathe, the water we drink, the sunlight, the good thoughts that influence our mind-body relationship, a healthy combination of exercise and rest, and the living food we eat. He explained the Krebs cycle, in which nutrients are converted to usable energy within the cell, which DNA uses to reproduce the cell or regenerate damaged tissues. In living food, such as raw fruits and vegetables, there is an ideal combination of phytonutrients, vitamins, minerals, enzymes, protein, fats, sugar and water. He believes that one cannot get a purer vitamin than what is found in this natural state. He patiently explained that the cooking process kills the foods by eliminating the enzymes and killing some of the phytonutrients as well as perhaps 70% of the vitamins. It also converts proteins, fats and minerals to a form the body cannot use. His bottom line is that the processed, cooked foods in the standard American diet are killing us, causing parasite invasion and nutritional deficiency, leading 70% of Americans to suffer from various chronic diseases.

For Dr. Rawdon, reversing a serious health crisis means total commitment to a changed life. He lectured on the importance of keeping body fluids at an alkaline pH level, about 7.5 in the optimal target zone, and the influx of life energy needed to make it happen. He also recommended a complete change in thought patterns as central to this life change. He told Cheryl that she had to have a positive outlook, as well as a strong belief that she could actually get better. Finally, he put together a regimen that included trampoline exercises, daily juicing, elimination of toxic chemicals and parasites, and unbelievably strict dietary guidelines. Cheryl was already a vegetarian, for all practical purposes. From now on, her vegan tendencies would become radical. There would be no sugar, no animal products whatsoever, and nothing cooked. Since Cheryl had already implemented 75% of the nutritional suggestions, we did not even raise an eyebrow.

There were also specific vitamin and enzyme recommendations to help jump start a healing response where systemic deficiencies existed. Dr. Rawdon teaches clients that a vitamin functions properly when it is in a natural state. Synthetic vitamins have a pharmacological or drug-like effect, but this is not the same as a physiological rebuilding process. In other words, in his view, if the vitamin label reads like a chemistry lesson, then it is synthesized and even potentially harmful. For a superior nutritional source of vitamins, minerals, and all the cofactors, one should make sure the label reads like a menu: wheat germ, carrot, buckwheat, etc. He strongly recommends whole food supplements to his patients. The charge for the session that day was minimal, but we did spend a fair amount of money on recommended supplements. All in all, however, it was a drop in the bucket compared to the massive sums demanded for cancer treatment by the conventional medical establishment.

Like many naturopathic experts, Dr. Rawdon believes that healing occurs in cycles. The body will not heal until adequate healing energies and nutrients are available. The more toxic the body, the less healing vitality there is available. The healthier the body, the more healing vitality is available. His own clinical reference guide says, "Once the body has gained enough energy that it can afford to both heal and carry on regular homeostatic responsibilities, the healing can begin. Fortunately the body has the intelligence to wait until the body can afford the energy for healing; otherwise death or compromised health would result."

According to recommendations made that day, Cheryl would also start taking specific measures to eliminate unwanted substances from the body. One of these methods was a weekly ionic cleanse treatment, commonly used in alternative clinics and health food stores. Trying it for the first time during the same visit, Cheryl placed her feet into a tub of water that was electrically charged, pulling out toxic chemicals. At first it seemed a bit *hocus pocus* to me, until I saw the water dramatically changing color. Even the doctor remarked how "orange" the solution had become. Cheryl shot back, with an allusion to what large servings of carrot juice do to a body, "Everything I do is orange!" It took him a few seconds to get her point, but when the thought fully sank in, he had a good laugh.

All in all, the man seemed impressive, and his philosophies were similar to our own. Perhaps the biggest factor, besides his expertise regarding the healing system, was the optimism he exuded. Though he outlined a specific plan of action, he didn't make any promises, and it was obvious Cheryl was in bad shape. But we walked out of the clinic feeling much better about her long-term chances. We were taking a proactive step that we believed may have been an answer to prayer.

She went right to work implementing the suggested strategies, and she stuck to them dutifully. She asked me to print up some index cards outlining what pills to take and when, and what procedures to follow at different times of day. There was something to do or consume almost every hour of the day. She would live on an intense combination of prayer, supplements, fresh air, clean water, exercise, more freshly extracted juice than she had ever consumed, uncooked oatmeal, raw fruits and vegetables, raw almonds, and a whole lot of love. She had already lost almost 20 pounds through chemo and surgery, and I was a bit concerned she would lose too much with these drastic measures. Even though she often felt deprived and tempted by "normal food," her weight stabilized and actually increased a bit. She felt better, and she started to look like her old self. In future visits to Tennessee, her vital signs also showed dramatic improvement, and Dr. Rawdon exuded even more optimism. Perhaps Cheryl derived a little "life energy" from his positive assessments. From all outward signs as well as specific test results, it appeared as if her body was responding.

A Husband's Prayer

LORD God, Father of mercies and God of all comfort,[1]

I am not a man of earthly wealth, but You have made me rich in faith and an heir of the kingdom.[2] I do not have great flocks and herds, but You have given me one little ewe lamb who is very precious to me.[3] Please, LORD, do not take her away!

No one can touch her with healing power like You can. I pray that You would take notice in heaven, and just say the word that would usher in healing and hope, recovery and rejuvenation. LORD, just say the word![4]

I know that neither life nor death, nor any other power, can separate us from Your love,[5] in Christ Jesus, and I pray that You would increase our faith,[6] strengthen our resolve, and calm our fears. We do not know what to do, but our eyes are on You.[7]

One day soon we look forward with great anticipation to living in a place where You will wipe away every tear from our eyes; and there will no longer be any death, or mourning, or crying, or pain.[8]

I pray for Your forgiveness, and for greater confidence that Your grace is all we need; for when we are weak, then we are strong.[9]

Please accept my thanksgiving and praise for hearing this prayer, and for granting what is best.

In Jesus' name, Amen.

---

[1] 2 Corinthians 1:3

[2] James 2:5

[3] 2 Samuel 12:3

[4] Luke 7:7

[5] Romans 8:38-39

[6] Luke 17:5

[7] 2 Chronicles 20:12

[8] Revelation 21:4

[9] 2 Corinthians 12:7-10

Chapter 10

Conventional Versus Natural Approaches

"He heals the brokenhearted and binds up their wounds." Psalm 147:3

"And the prayer of faith will save the one who is sick, and the Lord will raise him up. And if he has committed sins, he will be forgiven." James 5:15

"God heals, and the doctor takes the fees."
Benjamin Franklin

Cheryl's cancer forced me to do a massive amount of research into treatment options. The more I dug, the more I was confronted with some disturbing questions about mainstream cancer therapies. As previously stated, it is my belief that advances in modern medical science have blessed the lives of millions of people. Furthermore, Birmingham has a thriving medical industry and is a major hospital magnet in the South. I know a lot of Christians who are excellent doctors, researchers, nurses, and medical support personnel. They do their work as consummate professionals in a caring way. My frustration has more to do with the *system* than the people in it. My strong advice to someone with a life-threatening illness is to get a second opinion, find a doctor who can think *outside the box,* and explore available options in alternative medicine. There are three reasons why Christians facing this dilemma should not accept unquestioningly the recommendations of the medical establishment.

First, much of modern medicine is based on scientific materialism that is fundamentally at odds with the Bible. The biomedical model writes off the importance of the mind, not to mention the spirit, as will be explored in the next chapter. At a time when certain branches of science have reopened the question of God's superintendence of nature, *medical* science tends to look at human health in purely *physical* terms. The emphasis on how the body reacts to external stimuli in a laboratory setting creates a certain amount of tunnel vision in this regard. Much can be learned about physical reactions in experimental protocols, but human beings are more than laboratory rats! Dr. Dean Ornish, the cutting-edge cholesterol researcher, said it best: "Modern medicine is based on science, and scientists tend to believe only what can be measured and observed, even though what can be quantified may not be what is most important. Like the man who looks under the street lamp for his wallet 'because the light is better there' even though he lost it over in the dark alley, we may be looking in the wrong place if we study only what can be measured."[1] He suggested, "Physical heart disease may be the final manifestation of years of abuse that first begins in the psyche and spirit."[2] The same can be said of cancer, although there may also be complex environmental, genetic, and dietary factors at work.

Second, the devil has managed to poison most human enterprises with carnal influences, so why would anyone think that the medical system is immune? In fact, it is no secret that power and big money interests dominate the field. Cancer treatment is a mega-billion dollar industry, and there are huge profits and thousands of jobs at stake. FDA regulations and pharmaceutical profits, in many respects, drive the engine of what course of action doctors prescribe. Courageous physicians who dare to test the limits with alternative options expose themselves to the wrath of state medical boards. Besides, most natural approaches to ridding the body of cancer are more cost-effective and would not be financially appealing to the pharmaceutical industry. Successful alternative approaches pose a direct threat to the established bureaucratic system. For that reason, perhaps, even when a natural product has a track record of stellar results, great care must be taken in promotional representations, for fear of invoking the wrath of the FDA. If a treatment is not classified as a drug, it carries the standard caveat: "This product is not intended to diagnose, treat, cure or prevent any disease."

Our Tennessee nutritionist told us the story of a man who came to him with a cholesterol reading of 1,200. He was a walking heart attack! Dr. Rawdon put him on a diet very similar to Cheryl's, along with a tablespoon of cinnamon every day. A short time later, the man's cholesterol had dropped to under 200, without the help of any statin drugs. Doctors were baffled and amazed. Does anyone think the pharmaceutical industry will jump on the *cinnamon* bandwagon? There is no money in it.

Third, there have been two basic models of healing for centuries. The one that has thrived in western civilization is based on outside intervention. It proposes to treat the disease and eliminate the problem. The other model, more common to the east, suggests that the pathway to true health involves enhancing the body's own natural defenses. Chemotherapy is based on the first model, as it is designed to attack and eliminate the intruding cancer. In the process, its destructive force is equally damaging to healthy cells. It compromises the God-given immune system. Chemo does absolutely horrible things to a body! It is a useful treatment against some cancers, and perhaps it ought to be considered for short-term management of situations that might otherwise be deemed hopeless. I believe that one day, however, we will stop dripping poison into people's systems in order to *cure* them. Sooner or later, chemotherapy will go the way of *blood letting* and other barbaric practices in medical history.

Modern doctors go to medical school to learn the *intervention* model. They are not trained to deal much with nutritional issues. Their focus is more on sickness than wellness. When Cheryl was put into a clinical study to find out how certain breast cancers respond to chemotherapeutic agents, there was absolutely no monitoring of her diet. One would think that in a controlled study, researchers would be concerned about what participants put into their mouths, as if this might influence the results, but such was not the case.

When I was having some cholesterol problems, my personal physician prescribed two medications which, when used in tandem, can cause a tremendous amount of damage. I fired the doctor! My new doctor, who is a mainstream physician with alternative tendencies, encouraged me not to be so hard on the other man, since "he was only doing what he was trained to do." He charted a more natural course of action, and soon took me off prescription medications entirely. I added a tablespoon of cinnamon every day with my morning oatmeal, and my total cholesterol level dropped to 140, which is lower than it had ever been.

Why Christians Should Consider Natural Therapies

I am not dismissing the best that conventional therapy has to offer in spite of my skepticism, nor would I give a blank check to anything that passes for *alternative* therapies. The very fact that they are unregulated opens the door for false claims made by hucksters and quacks. Some alternative treatments, on the other hand, have a great deal of legitimacy, including documented studies in peer-reviewed journals. Appendix 1 gives the reader a good starting place to wade through the jungle of information, with citations of phenomenal books and websites.

Dr. Andrew Weil makes a powerful case that among the systems of the human body is one that goes unnoticed in the textbooks: a healing system. From the level of DNA to the cellular level to more complicated levels of biological organization such as tissue repair or natural reversals of atherosclerosis, the body shows an extraordinary ability to heal itself. "The healing system has a diagnostic capability; it can recognize damage… [It] can remove damaged structure and replace it with healthy structure."[3] According to Dr. Weil, people get sick when "the capacity of the healing system to restore balance [is] exceeded by the forces or circumstances of imbalance."[4] In other words, their natural defenses are overwhelmed. On the other hand, when a treatment works, it helps the body's own healing mechanisms to regain the upper hand. Dr. Weil believes, "All the circuitry and machinery is there. The challenge is to discover how to turn on the right switches to activate the process."[5]

The problem with cancer is that when it appears, even in the lower stages, it already represents a significant breakdown of the body's own healing arsenal. From this point of view, cancer is in many respects a *symptom* rather than a disease. The challenge of achieving a total cure, therefore, is formidable because the natural defenses are already compromised. The three mainstream therapies – surgery, chemotherapy, and radiation – attack an unwanted growth, but they do not deal with the root cause. For this reason, even if a cancer patient chooses conventional treatment, at the very least complementary approaches should be considered in order to support the healing system. Furthermore, many alternative-minded doctors would argue that the standard conventional treatments can actually impede what is left of the body's own healing mechanisms and should not be used at all.

Consider, for example, one of the most frequently cited alternative therapies, which involves raising fluid pH levels. Most cancer patients have a very low, or acidic, reading, while healthier individuals tend to be more alkaline. Cheryl's first alternative checkup revealed a pH level of 5.8, which is extremely acidic. In subsequent visits, it had climbed to 7.5, an optimum result. Otto Warburg won a Nobel Prize in 1931 for research into a respiratory enzyme. His basic conclusion regarding cancer was that it could be prevented if cells have adequate respiration, an issue directly related to pH levels. Cancer does not thrive in an oxygen-rich, alkaline environment. Warburg's findings were largely ignored, however, by the medical industry. In a stirring speech toward the end of his life in 1966, he argued, "There is no disease whose prime cause is better known, so that today ignorance is no longer an excuse.... That prevention of cancer will come there is no doubt, for man wishes to survive. But how long prevention will be avoided depends on how long the prophets of agnosticism will succeed in inhibiting the application of scientific knowledge in the cancer field. In the meantime, millions of men must die of cancer unnecessarily."[6]

Natural Strategies and God's Natural Provisions

In the aftermath of excruciating chemotherapy, disfiguring surgery, and smoldering radiation, Cheryl's program for returning to a state of wellness involved many diverse components. The one thing they all had in common can be summarized in a simple formula: *good stuff in, bad stuff out.* Every procedure and every step in her regimen were designed to strengthen her own God-given system and give her the best chance of survival. In many respects, there was nothing terribly complicated about the program. Dr. Weil says, "Healing requires energy. Energy is supplied by metabolism, the process of conversion of caloric energy in food to chemical energy that the body can use for its various functions."[7]

Cheryl harnessed the life-energy of the sun, oxygen, water, fresh fruits and vegetables, and other natural ingredients. The Bible teaches that the earth is cursed because of sin, and environmental poisons exist all around us, but we utilized *purified* air and water, organic produce, and sunlight – natural resources given by the Creator Himself in their purest state. We especially relied on the "pure spiritual milk" of God's Word and genuine prayer. The most important ingredient was recognition of God's hand, regardless of the outcome. *"The LORD sustains him on his sickbed; in his illness you restore him to full health"* (Psalm 41:3). Cheryl's specific regimen, including supplements, is found in Appendix 2, but the broad outline and general rationale for it is as follows.

As far as caloric intake is concerned, Cheryl flooded her system with freshly extracted fruit and vegetable juices. At the beginning of her diagnosis, we had an aging juicer, and my father gave us a newer, more efficient one that had been used by my mother five years previously. My father-in-law likewise was kind enough to purchase for us a portable blender for fresh fruit smoothies. Juicing is hard work and time-consuming. To remove dirt, parasites, and possible pesticide residue, all the produce has to be thoroughly washed. We use large tubs of water combined with a food-grade hydrogen peroxide solution, as well as a few drops of Shaklee Basic-H to do the job. Then every item has to be rinsed, dried, and cut. We often work for a couple of hours at a time and pour the juice into glass jars, which are then frozen. Every evening, Cheryl sets aside several jars for the following day's supply. Throughout the day, at regular intervals, she drinks the energy-bearing nutrients.

The juices consist primarily of the following combinations: carrot, carrot-celery, carrot-beet, apple, green bean, and cabbage. From time to time, we have tried other combinations and various recipes in juicing books, but we have stuck pretty much to these staples. Virtually all fresh fruits and vegetables raise pH levels, but carrot-celery juice is particularly effective in this regard. A lot of people cringe at the thought of drinking massive amounts of fruits and vegetables, but Cheryl enjoys apple and carrot juice. She never looked forward to green bean juice, and cabbage juice is even nastier to her taste buds, but it is reportedly very effective against parasites. The fresh apple juice is sometimes incorporated in a smoothie. We buy frozen berries and peaches, and often mix one of them with apple juice and a banana. It makes a delicious and very nutritional summertime treat.

As stated previously, Cheryl became a dedicated vegan. She craved "real food" at times, but for the most part adapted well to her diet. Giving up sugar was not as hard an adjustment for her as parting with meats and casseroles. Processed foods, all animal products (including milk, cheese and eggs), and sugar were taboo. Many of these foods – especially sugar – have an acidic effect on the body, lowering pH levels. Since cooking changes the fundamental chemistry of the enzymes, phytonutrients, and vitamins in food – and since her body needed every form of natural energy she could muster – that had to go as well. She survived largely on salads, fresh fruits, vegetables, grains, nuts, and sprouts. Many have asked, "Did she starve?" There were times when she was hungry, but the constant intake of "juice" calories helped to curb her appetite as well as maintain her weight. One should keep in mind that she was eating very few "empty" calories. She also started looking and feeling very well on this program, with plenty of energy, and she hardly ever caught a cold.

Food is not the only source of life-energy for the body's metabolic processes. Cheryl spent at least a half-hour a day out in the sun, taking in the rays that stimulate vitamin D production necessary for calcium absorption. Calcium and magnesium are valuable minerals, and they have pH-raising properties. Sunlight works synergistically with all that calcium-rich carrot juice! Too much sunlight can be detrimental, but a certain amount of it is extremely beneficial. Cheryl had to protect the part of her skin, up to the right side of her neck, which was subjected to five weeks of radiation, but she would sit outside for a half-hour reading her Bible or other good book. As long as the weather permitted it, she would take a daily walk for about 25 minutes, which is a terrific way of getting some sunlight.

Oxygen intake is important. Dr. Weil says, "Breathing may be the master function of the body, affecting all others."[8] The Bible certainly confirms that breathing is the essence of our being on earth. From the very beginning, "God formed the man of dust from the ground and breathed into his nostrils the breath of life, and the man became a living creature" (Gen. 2:7). When Abraham died, he is said to have "breathed his last" (Gen. 25:8). The Biblical terms *ruach* in Hebrew and *pneuma* in Greek refer to both the human spirit and the flow of air. In keeping with Warburg's respiration findings cited above, cancer cells hate oxygen. Fresh air is one of the best therapies to which a cancer patient can be exposed, and Cheryl spent a lot of time outside. In order to get rid of pollutants and fill our bedroom with negatively charged ions, we purchased a Fresh Air Machine, which does a great job of air purification. Cheryl also began a twice-daily routine of deep breathing exercises to take better advantage of this remarkable gift of God.

Water is essential to proper body functions. It flushes toxic chemicals and wastes out of our system, and it provides hydrogen and oxygen necessary for life. Dehydration, on the other hand, contributes to degenerative diseases. Cheryl began drinking several jars of juice a day, but she made sure to drink the equivalent of 10 to 12 glasses of water as well. Most of this was consumed in frequent, small sips rather than big gulps. She even brought a water bottle to church, which was not an attempt to be irreverent. It was simply a matter of continually watering her system and keeping it hydrated. The purity of the water was also an issue. We purchased a Shaklee reverse osmosis filtration system for drinking water. As for the shower head, we installed a special filter that removes chlorine.

Exercise was an important part of Cheryl's rehabilitation program. Rebounding and walking were the two primary components. We borrowed a trampoline from our friend, Bobbi, and essentially wore it out. Rebounding is a low impact exercise that is great for the lymphatic system. It increases the flow of lymph fluid by 15 to 30 times, carrying nutrients to cells and removing waste products. Walking through the neighborhood combines the benefits of fresh air, sunlight, and the most natural form of exercise. According to a Nurse's Health Study, published in the May 25, 2005 issue of the *Journal of the American Medical Association,* walking just three hours a week improves breast cancer survival rates by 50%. This is especially true for women who have hormone-responsive tumors.[9]

Occasional body massages nurtured the mind and body. Although we did not administer them as often as we should have, therapeutic massages helped ease Cheryl's joint pain after chemotherapy, stimulate her lymphatic pathways after surgery, ease her stress, and give her a feeling of relaxation and rejuvenation. All in all, they certainly promoted a sense of renewed energy and well-being.

Finally, there was the issue of *getting the bad stuff out,* particularly toxins, parasites, and the residual effects of chemo. Getting rid of toxins and metabolic waste material is essential to good health, even if the medical establishment pays little attention to it. We are continually bombarded with environmental pollutants and toxic chemicals in food, air and water. As stated above, Cheryl and I made every reasonable effort to eliminate the intake of contaminants and pesticides.

There remained the issue of how to get rid of *existing* toxic overload. Besides the massages, which help somewhat with toxic removal, Cheryl took four major steps. First, when she decided to go alternative one hundred percent, she started doing coffee enemas. As bizarre as the practice sounds, coffee enemas encourage the lower bowel and liver to eliminate toxins. It was somewhat funny, but when we told the second oncologist early on about our alternative tendencies, the doctor asked, "You're not doing coffee enemas, are you?" Cheryl shot back, "Of course not!" Little did she know, she would be doing them just a few months later.

Second, she did a weekly ionic cleanse, as mentioned in the previous chapter. This was generally done at our local health food store, *Honey and Spice.* Initially she underwent this therapy once a week and eventually once a month. Cheryl placed her feet in an electrically charged tub of water, pulling out toxins as the water changed color. Cheryl was determined to follow the Israelites of the Old Testament in exterminating "Hittites, Amorites, Jebusites, and *parasites."*

Third, Sarah Fultz had purchased a fairly expensive machine that did frequency specific acupuncture. Sarah believed it was instrumental in saving Sandlyn's life, and she started offering the service to others. Like the ionic cleanse, such machines are common in larger health food stores and among alternative practitioners. Cheryl enjoyed a nice visit with Sarah twice a week while the machine settings targeted the removal of breast cancer cells, yeast, and parasites.

Finally, there were specific supplements such as Okra Pepsin tablets and cabbage juice that facilitate parasite removal. Dr. Rawdon tells a story about a bear in the Smokey Mountains that was diseased and had to be eliminated. An autopsy revealed that the animal's intestinal tract had enough parasites to fill a five-gallon bucket. When park rangers urge campers not to feed animals their junk food, there is a good reason behind it. One cannot help but wonder, however, if the overly processed American diet is good for humans! Many experts make a strong case that toxins and parasites are major contributors to cancer.

None of these strategies is a guarantee of beating cancer. There are no guarantees in this life. However, in light of all these considerations, it was somewhat ironic and sad to have seen so many patients in the infusion centers digesting processed food and large amounts of sugar, even as chemo poisons were dripping into their systems. Many of them will die of cancer, and some of them will arguably die of ignorance.

Devotional Thoughts
"Why Christians Suffer"

The problem of human suffering is extremely complex. In the Bible, Job's friends are the champions of the simplistic solution: you suffer, therefore you must be a terrible sinner, and God is giving you your just desserts. Obviously, much needless suffering is brought on by all the evils that exist in the world. For example, wars claim the lives of innocent victims caught in the crossfire. God could have perhaps created a very different world, without the contingencies of free moral agency, but our existence would likely be very robotic. As it is, we are free to do good, and we are free to sin and hurt others. Many people suffer because of their own foolish choices, but that is not the end of the matter. Sometimes good people are subjected to pain that seems intolerable and unfair. Jesus' disciples asked the Savior about a man born blind: "Rabbi, who sinned, this man or his parents....?" Jesus replied, "It was not this man who sinned, or his parents, but that the works of God might be displayed in him" (John 9:2-3). Suffering, when properly handled, serves a larger purpose. It is an opportunity to display the "works of God." In the *bigger picture* of things, there are at least five Biblical reasons why Christians have to suffer.

1. To build our character.

James says, *"Count it all joy, my brothers, when you meet trials of various kinds, for you know that the testing of your faith produces steadfastness. And let steadfastness have its full effect, that you may be perfect and complete, lacking in nothing"* (James 1:2-4). Steadfast endurance is the ability to bear up under trial and withstand. We live in a world that wants to be insulated from pain. In some ways, though, there is truth to the old adage, "No pain, no gain."

Even the apostle Paul had to learn this lesson the hard way: *"Three times I pleaded with the Lord about this, that it should leave me. But he said to me, 'My grace is sufficient for you, for my power is made perfect in weakness.' Therefore I will boast all the more gladly of my weaknesses, so that the power of Christ may rest upon me. For the sake of Christ, then, I am content with weaknesses, insults, hardships, persecutions, and calamities. For when I am weak, then I am strong"* (2 Corinthians 12:8-10).

A Christian who is undergoing adversity can truly say, "God isn't finished with me yet." The writer of Hebrews compares our earthly fathers to our heavenly Father: *"For they disciplined us for a short time as it seemed best to them, but he disciplines us for our good, that we may share his holiness"* (Hebrews 12:10). Abigail Adams wrote to her son, John Quincy Adams, "It is not in the still calm of life or the repose of a pacific station that great characters are formed. The habits of a vigorous mind are formed in contending with great difficulties. Great necessities call out great virtues. When a mind is raised and animated by scenes that engage the heart, then those qualities which would otherwise lay dormant wake into life and form the character of the hero and the statesman."[10]

2. To magnify our sacrifices.

Someone said, "A crisis isn't what makes a person; a crisis shows what a person is made of." Paul says of the Macedonian Christians, *"For in a severe test of affliction, their abundance of joy and their extreme poverty have overflowed in a wealth of generosity on their part"* (2 Corinthians 8:2). That Lance Armstrong won the Tour de France seven times is an amazing feat, but the fact that he did it after coming back from cancer makes the story all the more remarkable. It is when people have to deal with seemingly insurmountable obstacles that others take notice (cf. Matt. 5:16).

3. To expand our influence.

Jesus warned His apostles: *"But before all this they will lay their hands on you and persecute you, delivering you up to the synagogues and prisons, and you will be brought before kings and governors for my name's sake. This will be your opportunity to bear witness"* (Luke 21:12-13). These disciples of the Lord would be subjected to a truth serum called martyrdom. They sealed their testimony with their own blood. As Tertullian would say a couple of centuries later, the blood of martyrs is the seed of the church.

4. To show the genuineness of our faith.

Peter says, *"In this you rejoice, though now for a little while, if necessary, you have been grieved by various trials, so that the tested genuineness of your faith – more precious than gold that perishes though it is tested by fire – may be found to result in praise and glory and honor at the revelation of Jesus Christ"* (1 Peter 1:6-7). Suffering is an opportunity for our faith to shine, so that neither we nor others will doubt our true allegiances.

5. To refocus our attention on God's Word.

The Psalmist says, *"It is good for me that I was afflicted, that I might learn your statutes"* (Psalm 119:71). Adversity forces our eyes on the words of the Bible. Its great truths suddenly mean more to us when we undergo a severe trial.

Have you ever noticed that the book of Acts revolves around a continual series of setbacks turned into stepping-stones? The obstacles become opportunities, each one summarized by a statement of growth, until we get to the final word in the book: "unhindered." No force on earth could stop the progress of the church, and adversity actually "served to advance the gospel" (Philippians 1:12).

The story is told of a man finding a butterfly cocoon. One day a small opening appeared, and he sat and watched the butterfly for several hours as it struggled to force its body through that little hole. Then it seemed to stop making any progress, as if it could go no farther. The man decided to help the butterfly, so he took a pair of scissors and snipped off the remaining portion of the cocoon. The butterfly then emerged easily, but it had a swollen body and small, shriveled wings. It was never able to fly. What the man in his generous haste did not realize is that the struggle required for the butterfly to get through the tiny opening was God's way of forcing fluid from the body into its wings so that it would be ready for flight.

Without struggles in life, we would be crippled spiritually. Consequently, *"we also exult in our tribulations, knowing that tribulation brings about perseverance; and perseverance proven character; and proven character, hope; and hope does not disappoint, because the love of God has been poured out within our hearts through the Holy Spirit who was given to us"* (Rom. 5:3-5).

---

[1] *Dr. Dean Ornish's Program for Reversing Heart Disease: The Only System Scientifically Proven to Reverse Heart Disease Without Drugs or Surgery* (New York: Baallantine Books, 1990), p. 28

[2] Ornish, p. 3

[3] Andrew Weil, MD, *Spontaneous Healing: How to Discover and Enhance Your Body's Natural Ability to Maintain and Heal Itself* (New York: Ballantine Books, 1995), p. 92

[4] Weil, p. 136

[5] Weil, p. 106

[6] Warburg, "The Prime Cause and Prevention of Cancer," http://www.whale.to/a/warburg.html

[7] Weil, p. 160

[8] Weil, p. 163

[9] "Walking Improves Breast Cancer Survival Rate," http://walking.about.com/od/cancerprevention/a/bc052005.htm

[10] David McCullough, "Knowing History and Knowing Who We Are," *Imprimis*, April 2005, p. 6

Chapter 11

Mind over Matter?

*"The apostles said to the Lord, 'Increase our faith!'
And the Lord said, 'If you had faith like a grain of
mustard seed, you could say to this mulberry tree,
"Be uprooted and planted in the sea," and it would
obey you.'"* Luke 17:5-6

*"Now may the God of peace himself sanctify you
completely, and may your whole spirit and soul and
body be kept blameless at the coming of our Lord
Jesus Christ."* 1 Thessalonians 5:23

Anthropologists typically define a human being in purely physical terms: brain volume of 1,400 cubic centimeters, bipedal locomotion, larynx positioning which makes vocal language possible, etc. Francis Crick, who together with James Watson discovered the structure of DNA, subscribed to this view. In the first sentence of a book on the subject, he said, "'You,' your joys and your sorrows, your memories and your ambitions, your sense of personal identity and free will, are in fact no more than the behavior of a vast assembly of nerve cells and their associated molecules."[1]

The Bible's definition is very different. Man is ultimately a spiritual being, created "in the image of God" (Gen. 1:27). Interplay exists between the spiritual and physical components of the whole person because the flesh is not all there is. This world is cursed, and life-threatening diseases would not threaten us if it were not for the introduction of human sin into the world (Gen. 3).

Adam and Eve, however, are not the only culprits. It is staggering to imagine the effects of *ongoing* sin on human health. Our rebellion, which starts in the mind, produces many adverse consequences. Instead of casting all our anxieties on God (1 Pet. 5:7), we would rather take matters into our own hands and literally worry to death. Rather than eating the perfect food God created for the human body, we prefer a diet of processed junk. We allow ourselves to be controlled by various addictions which harm the body. One of the central messages of the Bible is that human beings have done a remarkable job messing up a good thing. And yet even when God offers a solution to this terrible dilemma, we live in denial. Psalm 32 describes the very real *psychosomatic* impact of harboring unconfessed sin: *"For when I kept silent, my bones wasted away through my groaning all day long. For day and night your hand was heavy upon me; my strength was dried up as by the heat of summer"* (Ps. 32:3-4).

Of course, not all cancer can be attributed to personal spiritual deficiencies. Cheryl and I considered several possible contributors to her breast cancer, including multiple physical factors. Our speculations ranged from environmental toxins to unresolved emotional trauma in her past. Although we will never know in this life exactly what caused her cancer, we certainly believe the mental realm is often a major dynamic in serious illness.

If breakdown of health is facilitated by mental and

emotional dysfunctionality, one would expect that true healing must involve the *inside* as well. Is there a mind-body relationship in the healing process? Dr. Andrew Weil says, "In fact, relatively few in the medical establishment take the field of mind/body medicine seriously; and the most prestigious researchers, those who set priorities and influence funding, are contemptuous of colleagues who work in it."[2]

In researching for this chapter, I ran across an Internet article in which a highly respected medical doctor states, "Although many popular books on cancer talk about fighters and optimists, there's no scientific proof that a positive attitude gives you an advantage in cancer treatment or improves your chance of being cured." I strongly disagree, but such pronouncements do not surprise me. Again Dr. Weil says, "There is an increasing consensus in establishment science that mind is merely the product of the brain's circuitry and biochemistry, which we are on the verge of clarifying to the last detail. From this perspective, where mind is always an effect rather than a cause, scientists are unlikely to come up with ideas for studying how the mind might affect the body."[3]

It is not as if data for mind-body interaction is totally missing. A recent book by Jeffrey M. Schwartz and Sharon Begley demonstrates that the human mind is not merely a side effect of the brain's electrochemical activity. It is the other way around. Schwartz, a neuroscientist at UCLA, shows from two decades of research that the mind is an independent entity that can actually shape and influence the brain.[4] It is a major blow to scientific materialism and a finding totally consistent with Biblical Christianity.

Consider also the placebo response. In a *National Geographic* article, Joel Achenbach reviews several studies showing that placebo effects often produce real physical changes in the body. They are not "all in the mind." For example, 50 percent of Parkinson's patients showed improved motor function after receiving a placebo – a saline injection.[5]

Dr. Dean Ornish argues, "Our beliefs about what is possible – or impossible – often become a self-fulfilling prophecy. Until Roger Bannister ran a mile in less than four minutes, everyone thought it was impossible. Soon after, the four-minute mile became almost routine... Once people *believed* it was possible, it *was* possible."[6] In fact, a growing body of evidence from research studies specifically connects religious beliefs to better immune function, lower death rates from cancer, and better health behaviors.[7]

Mike, Cheryl and Brooke. Cheryl's hair has started
to grow back.

Almost every caregiver of those with life-threatening illness sees fighters who defy the odds and others who give up and resign, succumbing much earlier than expected. Mind-body factors do not tell the whole story, but they certainly play a much bigger role than some have thought. There are several dimensions to Cheryl's mental outlook that are worthy of note.

Resiliency

If there is one thing about my wife that constantly amazed me throughout this ordeal, it was her refusal to let cancer defeat her. Even when she was in excruciating pain, her motto was, "It's not as bad as it could be." She would then get up, put a smile on her face, and take on the challenges of the day. When it comes to having an unbeatable spirit, the apostle Paul had already set a remarkable example: *"We put no obstacle in anyone's way, so that no fault may be found with our ministry, but as servants of God we commend ourselves in every way: by great endurance, in afflictions, hardships, calamities, beatings, imprisonments, riots, labors, sleepless nights, hunger; by purity, knowledge, patience, kindness, the Holy Spirit, genuine love; by truthful speech, and the power of God; with the weapons of righteousness for the right hand and for the left; through honor and dishonor, through slander and praise. We are treated as impostors, and yet are true; as unknown, and yet well known; as dying, and behold, we live; as punished, and yet not killed; as sorrowful, yet always rejoicing; as poor, yet making many rich; as having nothing, yet possessing everything"* (2 Corinthians 6:3-10).

Optimism

Some patients want to know every detail of their disease, including every negative aspect of their prognosis. Unfortunately, many doctors are all too happy to flood patients with pessimism! It is akin to the negative placebo effect inflicted by a shaman or witch doctor in a primitive culture. Physicians must be truthful with patients, but they might have more success by instilling a degree of hope, helping their clients harness the power of the mind. Cheryl did not want to hear *anything* negative. In fact, there are a few things in the manuscript for this book that I actually had to cross out for her, because she simply was not interested in the gritty details. Her attitude has always been, "Can I possibly beat this? If so, what do I need to do?"

Strong Determination

Not very many people could stay on Cheryl's diet. It requires a high level of neuro-conditioning that associates pain (death) with cheating and pleasure (life) with sticking to the regimen. With major input from Dr. Day's videos and Dr. Rawdon, I put together a daily routine that Cheryl dutifully follows. Though she wants very much to go to heaven one day, she has a powerful incentive to continue life on earth for the moment. Although she enjoys good food, the desire to live outweighs the temptation to eat forbidden delicacies.

The transition was very difficult, since Cheryl was committed to preparing "normal" but semi-healthy meals for the rest of the family. We would sit down for supper, and the girls and I felt a certain amount of guilt eating in Cheryl's presence foods that she could not have. We did have to ban nachos-flavored tortilla chips from the house, at Cheryl's request, because she sneaked into the pantry closet and gave in to temptation. In the long run, the whole experience has all four of us eating a much healthier diet, and we often happily share a dinner of salad and vegetables.

Humor

The Bible says, "A joyful heart is good medicine, but a crushed spirit dries up the bones" (Proverbs 17:22). I've given several examples of Cheryl's quick wit throughout this book. There were moments of depression, but she never lost her sense of humor. While on a short trip in late-December 2004, we were tired, hungry, and searching for a place to eat. Our daughter Brooke spotted a Hooters restaurant and suggested playfully that we eat there. Cheryl said, "No, I've only got one *hooter,* and we're not going to eat where girls parade around with two perky ones." We all burst into laughter, and, needless to say, ate somewhere else.

On another occasion, after her mastectomy, we went to a Bunko party and Cheryl announced, "I want the *booby* prize!" If anyone can find a way to smile even in the midst of tragedy, Cheryl is able to do it. Periodically, she would give a new twist to historical eras: "Way back in B.C. – *before cancer.*" Anticipating her first mammogram after the mastectomy, she blurted out, "There's no *mammo* to gram!" When thinking about the curse of sin, as if speaking to Eve, she said, "Why did you have to eat the fruit?"

A funny incident occurred one afternoon while Cheryl was undergoing an ionic cleanse at the health food store. It was the time of day to take a fistful of pills, and she accidentally dropped one into the dirty water. A worker happened to walk by and see the foreign object floating around. Cheryl, never wasting an opportunity to pull someone's leg, said, "It came out of my foot!" After the girl gave her a look of incredulous shock, Cheryl confessed and they had a good laugh.

Gratitude

People often talk about *fighting* cancer, and military metaphors abound. Moreover, cancer diagnosis often causes people to be frustrated, angry, and profoundly depressed. Many of those who beat cancer learn to *accept* it and are *grateful* for the opportunity to reorder their lives. To the extent that a serious illness forces us to stop the rat race and get our priorities refocused, it can actually be a blessing.

Cheryl said, "When I feel sorry for myself, it means I'm not counting my blessings or thinking about others who are worse off than us." Philippians 4:4-7 says, *"Rejoice in the*

Lord always; again I will say, Rejoice. Let your reasonableness be known to everyone. The Lord is at hand; do not be anxious about anything, but in everything by prayer and supplication with thanksgiving let your requests be made known to God. And the peace of God, which surpasses all understanding, will guard your hearts and your minds in Christ Jesus." If Cheryl or I had a viable alternative, we would rather discover God's blessings without the adversity. Her cancer forced us to stop and notice how richly blessed we are. Grateful *acceptance* is a vital component of inner healing, and I believe it can actually influence physical healing.

Prayer

The preceding scripture in Philippians suggests that prayer and gratitude go together. I Peter 5:6-7 says, *"Humble yourselves, therefore, under the mighty hand of God so that at the proper time he may exalt you, casting all your anxieties on him, because he cares for you."* Prayer enabled Cheryl to lighten her burdens by handing them over to God. What a tremendous blessing! Of course, the act of prayer provides more than just a psychological benefit to the petitioner, including "the peace... which surpasses all understanding." On the receiving end of this communication is a God who is actually on the throne.

I am not suggesting that all of this was easy for Cheryl. There were moments of extreme anxiety and fear. She also wrestled with emotional issues that have plagued her most of her life. As she went about her business, however, she developed a quiet confidence that no matter what, all would be well.

Sermon Excerpt
"Building Faith in Lost Souls,"
preached many times over

Converting lost souls is a matter of building faith in people, as well as repairing defective faith. If people today had the *perfect faith* of Abraham (James 2:22), they would be Biblical Christians. It is only a lack of faith or a defective faith that would get in the way. How then can we help others' faith grow?

Biblical faith involves three sub-components: conviction, trust and surrender. Romans 10:17 says, "So faith comes from hearing, and hearing through the word of Christ." It is the gospel message which builds faith in the human heart. Biblical faith involves the total engagement of the person – intellectually, emotionally, and volitionally. *Conviction* takes place in the mind, *trust* occurs in the heart, and *surrender* is a matter of the will. How then do we make the case to lost men and women?

What is in God's Word that builds **conviction**? *Evidence!* A person who is struggling with intellectual issues needs to be exposed to the reasons why we believe the Bible is the truth of God, Jesus is the Son of God, and the gospel is the plan of God. Predictive prophecies, eyewitness testimony, and miracles should be considered – especially the resurrection of Christ. The purpose statement of the Gospel of John reads, "Now Jesus did many other signs in the presence of the disciples, which are not written in this book; but these are written so that you may believe that Jesus is the Christ, the Son of God, and that by believing you may have life in his name" (John 20:30-31). Of course, we must also patiently teach that reception of the evidence depends on the open-mindedness and hunger of those who weigh it. If legitimate testimony is thrown out of court before the case is heard, the wrong verdict will be reached. This is apparently what the rich man did with "Moses and the prophets" (Luke 16:27-31). He squandered his opportunity.

What element of the Bible's message builds **trust**? More than anything else, it is the trustworthiness of Jesus our Savior. Study His claims, consider His promises, and meditate on His manner of life. If one is willing to do this, doubts will evaporate. There are two trust issues that revolve around the salvation that Jesus offers us: 1) Is He *able* to save us eternally? 2) Is He *willing* to save us, in spite of our personal defects? Paul says of Abraham: "No distrust made him waver concerning the promise of God, but he grew strong in faith as he gave glory to God, fully convinced that God was able to do what he had promised" (Rom. 4:20-21). With regard to the second half of the equation, a leper asked Jesus, "Lord, if you will, you can make me clean. And Jesus stretched out his hand and touched him, saying, 'I will; be clean.' And immediately the leprosy left him" (Luke 5:12-13). Jesus is both *able* and *willing!* The Lord has a long track record of reliably supporting His saints in every trial. His promises never fail. You can bank on it!

What about **surrender**? The stubborn fellow may acknowledge faith in Christ, but he doesn't want to obey, so long as *God* is the one dictating the terms of compliance. Yet Jesus is the "source of eternal salvation to all who obey him" (Heb. 5:9). The Lord says, "If you love me, you will keep my commandments" (John 14:15). A faith that does not lead to total and complete surrender is warped and defective. People who really believe don't argue with God's requirements. They *obey* them.

In the end, the person who develops this kind of faith

knows he will be saved eternally, not because he deserves to be, but because the whole course of his life rests firmly on the gracious promises of God.

[1] Francis Crick, Astonishing Hypothesis: the Scientific Search for the Soul (Scribner, 1995), p. 3

[2] Andrew Weil, MD, Spontaneous Healing: How to Discover and Enhance Your Body's Natural Ability to Maintain and Heal Itself (New York: Ballantine Books, 1995), p. 111

[3] Weil, p. 111-112

[4] Jeffrey M. Schwartz and Sharon Begley, *The Mind and The Brain* (Reagan Books, 2003)

[5] "Resources: Who Knew?" National Geographic (August 2004), http://magma.nationalgeographic.com/ngm/0408/resources_who.html

[6] Dr. Dean Ornish's Program for Reversing Heart Disease: The Only System Scientifically Proven to Reverse Heart Disease Without Drugs or Surgery (New York: Baallantine Books, 1990), p. 30

[7] Harold G. Koenig, "Religion, Spirituality, and Medicine: Research Findings and Implications for Clinical Practice," *Southern Medical Journal*, Volume 97, Number 12, December 2004, p. 1195

Chapter 12

"Is it in Remission?"

"Strength and dignity are her clothing,
and she laughs at the time to come.
She opens her mouth with wisdom,
and the teaching of kindness is on her tongue.
She looks well to the ways of her household
and does not eat the bread of idleness.
Her children rise up and call her blessed;
her husband also, and he praises her:
'Many women have done excellently,
but you surpass them all.'
Charm is deceitful, and beauty is vain,
but a woman who fears the LORD is to be praised.
Give her of the fruit of her hands,
and let her works praise her in the gates."
Proverbs 31:25-31

After Cheryl's conventional therapy ended, she started looking radiant again. Her attitude was positive, her laughter never completely went away, her hair grew back, and her outer appearance improved dramatically. People just assumed she was better and the worst had passed. A few churches known to us actually announced, somewhat presumptuously, that Cheryl had turned the corner and was on the mend. If we could only have been so certain ourselves! That said, as Cheryl committed herself to the natural regimen, and we gave ourselves to prayer, even we were cautiously optimistic about her chances.

Once in awhile, however, someone would ask, "The cancer is in remission, isn't it?" How does a person with a life-threatening illness this dangerous answer a question like that? Cheryl had essentially been given a death sentence by her first oncologist. Her surgeon said that there was a "significant chance" it would return. The second oncologist suggested that if the cancer metastasized, survival would no longer be the treatment goal. Her radiologist, who is a very compassionate person, put the matter in God's hands. Statistics for inflammatory breast cancer are bleak, and Cheryl had a bad case. Were we living in the calm before the storm? Outwardly, things looked hopeful, but inside Cheryl's body, were insidious tumors forming? Was the gauntlet about to come down? We simply did not know!

We had absolute confidence in God's love and His power to heal, but we could not presume to know His will in the matter, or to decide the outcome on our own. We lived in complete limbo, with a huge cloud overhead, not knowing how it would all turn out. As a husband, I did not know if I would have a wife, or if the girls would have a mother, from one season to the next. Every time Cheryl had a stomach ache, leg cramp, or headache, was it a potential time bomb about to go off? The final resolution would become transparent if and when the cancer returned, but there would be no such resolution if the cancer was sufficiently contained and defeated. How does one celebrate a victory when he doesn't even know the score?

As Sarah Fultz says, everyone lives with uncertainty about this life, but for some of us, the uncertainty is more "in your face." 1 Peter 5:7 says, "Casting all your anxieties on him, because he cares for you." Sarah adds that in fighting cancer, "You work as if everything depends on what you're doing, and live as if everything depends on God." That sums it up well. Randy Harrison, our cardiologist friend and brother in Christ, suggests that every day is a gift of God. If we count each day as a gift, we take nothing for granted. That is the approach Cheryl took, and it allowed her to overcome her fears and truly *live* again.

Still, the periodic doubts resurfaced occasionally. The conventional doctors could not tell us much. Cheryl had already received more than enough radiation, and it was not the policy of her UAB doctors to do regular scans. In the follow-up visits, doctors would do a surface check for evidence of tumors and ask the standard questions: "Have you had any headaches? Any bone pain? Any trouble breathing? Any abdominal cramps?" It all had to do with cancer recurrence in the target zones of the brain, bones, lungs, or liver. On one visit, the oncologist thumped Cheryl's stomach, and my wife blurted out, "It sounds like a watermelon!"

On Monday, June 20, 2005, we visited Dr. Rawdon in Hohenwald, Tennessee. Cheryl posed the question herself, almost holding her breath: "Do you think I'm in remission?" Dr. Rawdon has a remarkable grasp of the human body and its healing system, but we would never hold him medically responsible for venturing an opinion of this nature. He had studied Cheryl's UAB blood tests, run some tests of his own, put Cheryl on a proven regimen, and witnessed her improvement. Upon hearing his nervous client's question, he paused several seconds to search for the right words. He then said, *"Better* than remission.... God is good!"

Several years earlier, Dr. Rawdon was sought out by so many people who were being cured by his advice that he decided to quit his pharmacy practice and devote his fulltime efforts to consulting people about health and healing through natural therapies. His track record of helping seemingly hopeless cases is truly remarkable, and his eyes light up when he talks about some of the success stories. Would Cheryl Wilson be another one of them?

This book is being published – some would say *prematurely* – with the full realization that there are no guarantees in this life. Ecclesiastes 9:11 says that "time and chance happen to them all." Cheryl's earthly life will come to an end sooner or later. The inevitable fate awaits everyone. Our *ultimate hope* and *final resolution* are not fixated on a planet cursed by sin. Paul writes, *"If then you have been raised with Christ, seek the things that are above, where Christ is, seated at the right hand of God. Set your minds on things that are above, not on things that are on earth. For you have died, and your life is hidden with Christ in God. When Christ who is your life appears, then you also will appear with him in glory"* (Col. 3:1-4). For Christians who trust the Savior with every fiber of their being, the ultimate outcome is not in doubt. Whatever happens in this life, it is a win-win situation, and there is a happy ending.

Who are the heroes in this story? Will Rogers once said, "We can't all be heroes because somebody has to sit on the curb and clap as they go by." In this particular case, the applause would last awhile because the parade line is long. Cheryl is a personal hero, a little woman with a big heart. Like the *worthy woman* of Proverbs 31, she certainly "smiles at the future" (31:25 *New American Standard Version).* The saints of God who have rallied to our aid are some of the finest people on the face of the earth. I want the world to know what it is missing by not being a part of God's family.

Finally, I yearn to say something about the LORD Himself. He is truly Cheryl's "Shepherd," and mine (Psalm 23:1). One of my prayers has been a promise that if God should heal my wife, I would write something that extols His greatness. I added that if in His infinite wisdom the LORD should take her home, I would still try to find a way to publish His greatness to the world. Psalm 40:10 declares, *"I have not hidden your deliverance within my heart; I have spoken of your faithfulness and your salvation; I have not concealed your steadfast love and your faithfulness from the great congregation."* This book is a feeble attempt to keep that promise.

A much healthier-looking Cheryl,
with the author

Sermon Excerpt
"Using Ecclesiastes in Evangelism,"
preached many times over

Ecclesiastes is about our purpose in life. This fascinating little book closes with the words: *"The end of the matter; all has been heard. Fear God and keep his commandments, for this is the whole duty of man. For God will bring every deed into judgment, with every secret thing, whether good or evil"* (12:13-14). For many years I taught this passage without realizing its fundamental implication. Life is a probationary period for a day of reckoning, beyond which we will be rewarded or punished. We need Judgment Day as an affirmation of our basic worth as human beings.

Before his death, scientist Carl Sagan wrote a book, *Pale Blue Dot.* Reacting to a picture of earth taken by a Voyager spacecraft several billion miles away (hence the title), he writes, "Our posturings, our imagined self-importance, the delusion that we have some privileged position in the Universe, are challenged by this point of pale light. Our planet is a lonely speck in the great enveloping cosmic dark. In our obscurity, in all this vastness, there is no hint that help will come from elsewhere to save us from ourselves."[1] It is a dismal appraisal of man's inherent worth and value. Nevertheless, if God is taken out of the equation, Mr. Sagan is exactly right. Without Judgment Day, then we are nothing but specks of dust in a universe so gigantic that it staggers the imagination.

On the other hand, how different is the perspective of a believer! With an ultimate day in court with the Almighty awaiting us, eternity hangs in the balance. In that case, every word, every action, and every thought are suddenly invested with eternal importance. The point is that our purpose in life is inextricably tied to the Judgment. There is no getting around it. Only a believer in the God of the Bible has a firm basis for knowing why he is here, where he is going, and why his life is worth anything of lasting value.

---

[1] Carl Sagan, *Pale Blue Dot: A Vision of the Human Future in Space* (Ballantine Books, 1997), p. 7

Appendix 1

Helpful Books, Websites and Products

While dealing with Cheryl's cancer, we ran across hundreds of invaluable books and websites. The following list includes the ones we found most helpful. In each category, our favorite source is listed first.

Alternative Healing Books (General Introductions)

- Andrew Weil, M.D. *Spontaneous Healing: How to Discover and Embrace Your Body's Natural Ability to Maintain and Heal Itself* (Ballantine Books, 1995). A phenomenal book and great place to start.
- Gary Null, Ph.D. *The Complete Encyclopedia of Natural Healing: A comprehensive A-Z listing of common and chronic illnesses and their proven natural treatments* (Bottom Line Books, 2001). The sections on cancer and breast cancer are very helpful.
- James A. Duke, Ph.D. *The Green Pharmacy: New Discoveries in Herbal Remedies for Common Diseases and Conditions from the World's Foremost Authority on Healing Herbs* (St. Martin's Press,

1997). The title speaks for itself.
- Jordan S. Rubin, N.M.D., C.N.C. *Patient Heal Thyself: A Remarkable Health Program Combining Ancient Wisdom with Groundbreaking Clinical Research* (Freedom Press, 2003). An interesting read from the author of *The Maker's Diet.*

Alternative Healing Websites (Cancer)
- www.alternative-cancer.net – a complete beginner's guide to the world of natural, alternative cancer treatments. Get the eight-page condensed version free, or order the full report for $19.75. This is a must-read starting place for victims of cancer.
- www.naturalhealthschool.com/acid-alkaline.html - read about pH balance and what to do if you're too acidic.
- www.annieappleseedproject.org – a comprehensive site, with valuable links, for those interested in complementary, alternative medicine (CAM) for cancer.
- www.cancer-prevention.net – nine effective, natural strategies to kill your cancer.
- www.doctormurray.com – helpful material on alternative approaches to cancer. Chemotherapy patients should consult Dr. Murray's guide to supplementation at www.doctormurray.com/articles/chemotherapy.htm
- www.DrDavidWilliams.com – a good general introduction to alternative therapies by the author of *Alternatives* newsletter.

Inflammatory Breast Cancer Websites
- www.ibcresearch.org – this is a definitive, must-read website for victims of inflammatory breast cancer.
- www.ibcsupport.org – another equally valuable site

for this rare form of breast cancer.

- www.imaginis.com/breasthealth/inflammatory.asp – a good brief description of IBC, with helpful links.
- www.breastcancer.org – perhaps the most beneficial general-purpose breast cancer site on the Internet.

Ordering Information for Helpful Products

- **www.osasgarden.com** is Dr. Rawdon's site. Highly Recommended.
- www.drday.com – **Dr. Lorraine Day's videos** about beating cancer naturally are insightful. Check them out at her official site.
- www.allensclub.com – special prices for cancer patients on **Barlean's Lignan Flax Oil.**
- www.barleygreensupply.com – **Barley Green** is a great source of green nutrients, and this merchant sells it at a very reasonable cost. Also available is a Beta Carrot powder that is a good carrot juice substitute when traveling away from home.
- www.dfwx.com/h2o2.html - great prices on food-grade hydrogen peroxide for cleaning fruits and vegetables.
- www.**freshairmachine**.com – the air purifying machine we use. It's priced competitively and it combines five cutting-edge technologies to deliver fresh air.
- www.**swansonvitamins**.com – where we buy a lot of our vitamins at steep discounts.
- Cheryl used **Miracle II** products with great success: the moisturizing soap for bathing, the neutralizer for skin care and raising pH levels, and the lotion for post-surgery scars and radiation burns. All proved extremely helpful. Email Zozula@LHTC.net for the best prices that we have found. See www.miracleii.com for the company website.

- **Shaklee** has several products that are useful against cancer. We especially like Shaklee Basic-H for cleaning vegetables, the BestWater reverse-osmosis filtration system, Optiflora Prebiotic Complex, and Super Cal Mag Plus, which is great for raising pH levels. See www.shaklee.com for the company website. Our favorite distributor is Sarah Fultz, whose number is (205) 680-6077.

- **Juice Plus+** produces a variety of whole food products that supplement a juicing regimen. We like the Garden Blend, Orchard Blend, and Vineyard Blend formulas – almost like eating your fruits and vegetables in pill form. See www.juiceplus.com for details, or call our favorite distributor, Beverly Wilson, at (408) 275-0321.

- www.standardprocess.com is the website for the company that produces supplements for natural-healing practitioners, including Dr. Rawdon. Many of the supplement formulas mentioned in Appendix 2, and designed to target specific system deficiencies, originate at **Standard Process**.

- Two of the best Internet sources for Standard Process supplements are **www.costlesssupplements.com**, which sells them for 26% off; and **www.myhealth-store.com**, which sells them at 20% off, with free shipping on orders over $99.

- www.cellquest.com – The **CellQuest** dietary liquid supplement is extracted naturally from the world's largest herb and contains a wide range of phytochemicals. Its polysaccharides, polyphenols and phytoalexins (plant defensive compounds) have generated significant interest as immune-system boosters in the fight against cancer. One of our relatives believes CellQuest helped to save her father's life. For phone orders, call 1-877-565-5566.

- The **Champion Juicer** is a slow-speed, masticating type machine, giving more fiber, enzymes, vitamins and trace minerals than the typical juicer. Contact the Plastaket Manufacturing Company at www.champion juicer.com, call (866) 935-8423, or purchase one at your local health food store.

Appendix 2

Cheryl's Daily Regimen

We printed out the following schedule on index cards –
one for each period of the day. It is a brutal regimen,
in many respects, but Cheryl followed it like a trooper.

Early morning
   5:30 am
      Cellquest
   6:30
      2 Cantotrophin Plus, 2 Cantolytin Cleanse,
      2 Zoezyme, 1 Coral Calcium (or 3 Shaklee
      Calcium) with water
      Morning Prayer, Bible reading, and preparations for
      juicing (if no frozen juices have been thawed)
   7:15
      Breakfast with 2 tablespoons Flaxseed
   8:00
      3 Thytraphin PMG, 1 B-Complex, 2 Okra Pepsin,
      1 Prebiotic complex (pill and powder),
      1 Dermatrophin PMG, 1 Cellular Essentials,
      1 Grape Seed, 1 Shark Cartilage, 1 Alpha
      Lipoic Acid, 1 Ester-C, 1 Co-Q10, and 1 Curcumin

with Carrot-Celery juice and Barley
Green
EXERCISE – more water

Midmorning
9:00 am
Apple juice with 20 drops of Phosfood / also, 1 tbsp
coconut oil
ENEMA # 1
10:00
2 Cantotrophin Plus, 2 Cantolytin Cleanse,
2 Zoezyme with Romaine-beet-tomato juice
and/or Green bean juice
GOOD THOUGHTS! And more water!

Midday
11:00 am
Cellquest
Noon
Lunch with 2 tablespoons Flaxseed
1:00 pm
2 Cantotrophin Plus, 2 Cantolytin Cleanse,
2 Zoezyme, 2 Okra Pepsin, 1 Prebiotic
complex (pill and powder), 1 Dermatrophin PMG,
and 1 Co-Q10 with Carrot juice and
Barley Green

Midafternoon
2:00 pm
Apple juice with 20 drops of Phosfood
2:30
More water!
3:00
Carrot Juice and Barley Green with 1 Calcium

Dinnertime
>4:15 pm
>>Cellquest
>
>5:15
>>2 Cantotrophin Plus, 2 Cantolytin Cleanse,
>>2 Zoezyme with Romaine-beet-tomato juice
>>and/or Green bean juice
>
>5:30
>>Dinner with 2 tablespoons Flaxseed
>
>6:15
>>3 Thytraphin PMG, 1 B-Complex, 2 Okra Pepsin,
>>1 Prebiotic complex (pill and powder),
>>1 Dermatrophin PMG, 1 Cellular Essentials,
>>1 Grape Seed, 1 Shark Cartilage, 1 Alpha
>>Lipoic Acid, 1 Ester-C, 1 Co-Q10, and 1 Curcumin
>>with Carrot-Celery juice and Barley Green
>>ENEMA # 2

Late evening
>7:00 pm
>>More water
>
>8:15
>>2 Cantotrophin Plus, 2 Cantolytin Cleanse,
>>2 Zoezyme with green bean juice or apple
>>juice (with 20 drops of Phosfood) or Smoothie with
>>Apple juice (and Phosfood)
>
>9:15
>>Cellquest / Set out frozen juices for the following
>>day
>
>10:15
>>2 Okra Pepsin, 1 Coral Calcium (or 3 Shaklee
>>Calcium), 1 Pinealplex (or 2-3 Melatonin) with
>>water

Appendix 3

For Breast Cancer Victims Only: "Inflate-a-Boobs"

A fter Cheryl's mastectomy, Elaine Laurence sent her the following note, with a bag full of colored balloons. It was the perfect comic relief at an emotionally draining time. Elaine is a dear sister in Christ and an inflammatory breast cancer survivor herself. She is the sister of Lanning Courtney, who was a gospel preacher, and is an esteemed ladies' Bible class teacher. Her outward demeanor is respectful and conservative. You'd never know it, though, from the following message!

Welcome to the world of Inflate-a-Boobs!

Inflate-a-Boobs are the perfect solution for YOU!

Since you inflate them yourself… they are always the **perfect** size.

Our wide range of colors makes it possible to color coordinate with many of your outfits!

(If you live in the southern region of the United States, however, the color white cannot be worn after Labor Day.)

Caution: If you will be wearing only one Inflate-a-Boob, please do not use helium, as this may lead to one "perky" and one that "just hangs around."

We at Inflate-a-Boob hope you enjoy our product and we promise that we will continue our research to bring you the best inflatable product we can.

Elaine Laurence, Ph.D. of B, MS in I, and Head of Research (I.W.O.MS.)*

---

*Doctor of Boobology, Master in Inflatology, Head of Research (I wore one myself)

Used by permission.

Appendix 4

A Sister's Prayer

The following prayer is by Julie Jamerson, a sister in Christ at Edward's Lake.

Jehovah God,
Merciful and loving,
Giver of life and breath to all men;
Compassionate Father, who knows the needs of His children, and who is ready to provide for them all good things,

What a comfort to come before You and cast our care on You. How truly blessed we are to be Your people! How secure we feel to be cared for by the Creator of Heaven and Earth! We read in Your word of Your mighty works. We see the awesome power that You alone possess. You appoint rulers for the nations, and rule in the affairs of men. And yet we also read that Your eye is on the tiny sparrow, and that You take the time to clothe the lilies of the field. How great and magnificent You are!

And so, Father, we come to You with confidence both in Your ability and in Your desire to care for us, bringing to

You our concerns for one of Your own, our sister Cheryl Wilson.

We acknowledge before You our smallness and our ignorance. We do not pretend to understand why she has become ill with cancer. We do know that You love her, and that You hold her life in Your hands. We recognize that we are all completely dependent on You. You have all wisdom and understanding – You see the best course for all things, and our vision is so limited. We pray that *Your will* be done in all things, and not ours.

We also understand that You have taught us to ask for the things we need and want. So please incline Your ear to us, and hear our prayer for Cheryl, Father, and grant the things we ask according to Your will.

First, we would remind You of her example of faithfulness among Your children. Remember her love and service to her family. Remember her love and service to the congregations where she and Mike have worked so diligently. Remember her generous spirit and her joy in living the life You have given her.

Father, we ask that You would heal Cheryl's body. Please make her well again. Please restore her health completely so that she can once again serve You and others with energy, as she has done so effectively in the past.

Please give her courage and stamina to face the treatments that are intended to heal her. In the moments when she is hurting, ease her pain. In the moments when she is fearful, hold her hand and calm her. And in the moments when she is tired, allow her to rest in You.

Grant her the grace to trust in You fully. Give her the peace that surpasses all understanding – the peace which comes from knowing that she belongs to You, so that she can face each day with the assurance of Your love, and be strengthened.

Please comfort Cheryl, Father. Comfort her through the promises in Your word to care for those who are Your children. Comfort her through loving acts of kindness and caring from friends and family. And comfort her through the prayers of brothers and sisters in Christ whom she may not even know personally, but who are concerned for her *because* she belongs to You.

Father, we want to commit to You to care for Cheryl ourselves, as far as we are able. Grant us, her friends and family, the wisdom to do the things which will be the most helpful and meaningful to her. Give us the words that will uplift her, as well as words that will calm and comfort her. Help us to show our love and concern for her in ways in which she will feel it. We want so much to be of service to her – please aid us in caring for her.

Please bless Cheryl's family, Lord. Strengthen Mike, and give him courage as he goes through this with her. Please bless Megan and Brooke with peace, calmness, and a very real sense of Your presence with them. Give them all grace to shoulder the day to day activities of caring for her in a way that honors her as the godly wife and mother she is.

Finally, Father, please use this illness as an occasion for Your glory. May Cheryl, Mike and the girls, and all of us conduct ourselves through this in a way that shines Your light brightly in this world. Upon observing Cheryl, help others who do not yet know You to become convinced of Your care for Your children. Help them to be impressed by

Your wisdom in designing the relationships of family, and the church family. Use this event to create a desire in them to learn more about You, and to want to serve You, because of the examples of these Christians they have observed in such circumstances.

We love Cheryl, Father, and we beg You to deliver her from her illness. Care for her, and bless her. Almighty God, carry her on wings of eagles. Help her to run and not be weary – may she walk and not faint.

Be merciful to us, and hear our prayer for Cheryl,
For we ask in Jesus' name,

Amen

Scripture Index

Ezekiel
16:6 – 47

Daniel
6:22 – 47
9:23 – 47

Malachi
3:10 – 78, 80
4:6 – 59

New Testament

Matthew
5:16 – 112
6:33 – 83
28:18-20 – 75

Mark
5:25-27 – 29
6:31 – 61
10:29-30 – 70
10:51 – 75

Luke
5:12-13 – 124
6:38 – 84
7:7 – 98
8:14 – 66
16:22 – 40
16:27-31 – 66, 124
17:5 – 98
17:5-6 – 115
21:12-13 – 112

John
5:6 – 21
9:2-3 – 111
13:35 – 69
14:15 – 124
20:30-31 – 123

Acts
2:42 – 75
8:39 – 86
20:35 – 37
24:24-25 – 66
28:31 – 113

Romans
1:16 – 75
3:23 – 67
4:20-21 – 124
5:1-5 – 25
5:3-5 – 114
8:31-39 – 19
8:35 – 20
8:38-39 – 98
10:17 – 123
12:10 – 56
12:9-13 – 69

1 Corinthians
1:10 – 75
9:22 – 75

2 Corinthians
1:3 – 98
1:11 – 85
4:8-9 – 85

4:15 – 85
5:6-10 – 26
6:3-10 – 119
8:2 – 112
9:11-12 – 84
9:15 – 75
12:7-10 – 98
12:8-10 – 111
12:10 – 49

Ephesians
3:14-21 – 75
4:12 – 75
4:13 – 75
4:18 – 66
5:22-24 – 56
5:25-29 – 57
6:2 – 56

Philippians
1:12 – 113
4:4-7 – 26, 121

Colossians
3:1-4 – 130
3:21 – 56

1 Thessalonians
5:23 – 115

1 Timothy
5:14 – 78

2 Timothy
2:2 – 75

Titus
2:5 – 78

Hebrews
5:9 – 124
12:10 – 112
13:5-6 – 67
13:6 – 41

James
1:2-4 – 111
1:6-7 – 113
2:5 – 98
2:22 – 123
4:14-17 – 26
5:14 – 18
5:15 – 99
5:16 – 43

1 Peter
1:3-4 – 48
4:11-12 – 75
5:6-7 – 122
5:7 – 116, 128

2 Peter
3:9-10 – 66
3:18 – 75

Revelation
21:4 – 98